5" YEAR READING LEVEL

? USE FOR 6" YR.

Ricky Sutter

The Crowded House

and other tales

BY

FAN KISSEN

Script Writer and Program Consultant
Elementary School Division
WNYE, Board of Education Station
New York City

BOSTON
NEW YORK
CHICAGO

HOUGHTON MIFFLIN COMPANY
The Riverside Press Cambridge

DALLAS
ATLANTA
SAN FRANCISCO

PRINTED IN THE U.S.A.

Contents

Things You Will Want to Know

Why are these stories called Tales from the Four Winds?

The four winds come from the north, south, east, and west. The stories in this book come from many different places too. They come from countries all over the world.

Most of these stories are so old that no one knows who first told them or where they were first told. We do know that for hundreds of years, the same stories have been told over and over again.

Sometimes a story that comes from one land reminds you of a story that grew up in another land. In Japan, you might hear the tale called *One-Inch Fellow.* It is very much like *Tom Thumb*, an English tale. In China children like to hear the story of *The Feast of Lanterns*, which is very much like *Rip Van Winkle*, a story told in the United States.

No matter what land the story comes from, the people in the story who are polite, honest, and kind are always rewarded, but dishonest, selfish, or cruel people are punished.

As we read these stories, we can see that people all over the world are really very much alike. They laugh at the same things, cry at the same things, like the same good things, and hate the same bad things.

What can you do with these stories?

You can read these tales silently by yourself, just as you would read any story, but you will enjoy them even more if you take part with others in reading them aloud.

One group in your class might use any one of these tales as a make-believe radio program for the others in the class to listen to. The tales in this book were written as radio plays, and they have really been used on a radio station as a program for children.

Your class might have a make-believe radio program to which other classes in the school could be invited. You can even have a real radio program if there are loud-speakers in the classrooms in your school.

What might you do in a radio play?

When you take part in a radio play, you may have one of many different parts. You may have a great deal to say, you may have only a little to say, and you may not say a word.

You may be one of the *cast*. The cast is the name for all those who take the parts of the people in the story. When you take the part of a person in a radio play, you read everything that the person says. You try to read it just the way the person would say it.

You may be the *announcer*. The announcer tells the name of the play and something about the story. He also tells when the play is over. If you are giving the play for another class or for part of your own class, the announcer tells the names of those who took part. He reads all the parts that come after the word ANNOUNCER.

In each of these plays there is a part for the *narrator*. *Narrator* is just another word for story-teller. In a radio play, not all of the story is told by reading the things which the people in the story say. The narrator tells the parts of the story that are not read by the cast. He reads everything that comes after the word NARRATOR.

Perhaps you would like to be the *sound man.* When you listen to plays over the radio, you hear many different sounds. You may hear horses galloping or rain falling. Of course you know that there are not real horses galloping around the studio and that it isn't really raining. Those sounds are made by the sound man.

If you are the sound man, you must watch for the word SOUND in the play. You must be ready to make the sound that you are told to make there.

At the beginning of each play, you will find a list of the sounds which are needed. You will also find pictures which show you how to make the sounds.

Before the play begins, be sure that you have ready all the things you need to make those sounds. Some sounds, such as the moo of a cow, are made by the voice of one person. If there are many different sounds in one play, more than one sound man may be needed.

Every radio play needs someone to be in charge of the music. We might call him the *music man.* If you are the music man, you must have music ready for each place in the play where you see the word MUSIC. The music may be made by playing part of a record, or children may sing or hum part of a song that fits the story.

What do such words as (Bridge), (Laughs), and (Up) mean when they are printed in italics and are in parentheses?

Bridge: In a play on the stage, the curtain is closed between parts of a play. The audience can't see what is going on in a radio play, so music is played between the parts. This music is called a bridge. It carries you across from one part of the play to the next.

Up, Out, and Under: You will sometimes find the word *up*, or *out*, or *under* after MUSIC and with the words which tell what sound is to be made.

The word *up* means that the sound or music should begin or should be made louder.

The word *out* means that the sound or music should stop.

The word *under* means that the sound or music should go on but should be very soft so that the person who is reading can be heard.

Sometimes you will find some words in parentheses ( ) before or among the words which you are to read. These words should not be read aloud.

Sometimes the words will tell you how to read what comes next, as (*Slowly*). Other times they will tell you something you should do, such as (*Laughs*) or (*Weeps*).

When you come to the word (*Fade*), it means that your voice should grow softer.

(*Fade in*) means that your voice should be soft at first and then grow louder.

(*Off mike*) means that your voice or the sound should sound as if it came from far away.

Now you know what these words mean, and you know what each person has to do in a radio play. You are ready to have your own radio plays and perhaps a make-believe radio station to broadcast the *Tales from the Four Winds*.

Clever Manka

CAST	JOSEF	MANKA
	FARMER HOLTZ	ANNOUNCER
	JUDGE	NARRATOR

SOUNDS

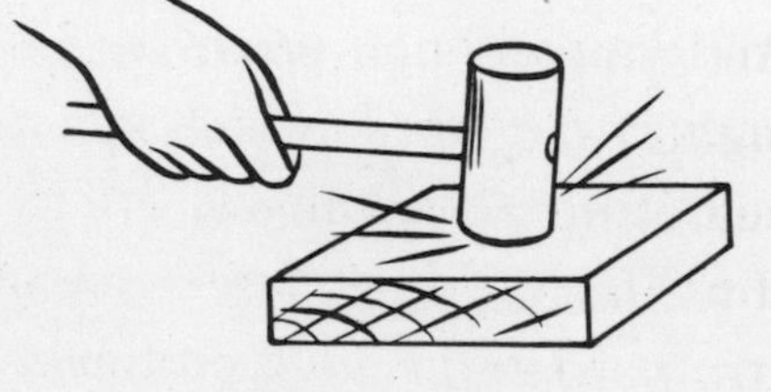

Pounding of gavel

ANNOUNCER: Hello, boys and girls, it's story time. Today you will hear a story from Czechoslovakia. It is about a girl who was very clever, especially at guessing riddles. The name of the story is *Clever Manka*.

MUSIC: (*Up and out*)

NARRATOR: There once lived in Czechoslovakia a rich farmer named Holtz who became rich by driving hard bargains and trying to get the best of everyone with whom he did business. But a clever girl called Manka forced him to keep one bargain he had made.

Now Manka's father, Josef, was a shepherd who was hired by Farmer Holtz to shear his sheep. The farmer promised to give Josef a calf for his work. When the job was finished, (*Fade*) the shepherd went to the farmer and said,

JOSEF: Well, Farmer Holtz, I have finished shearing your sheep.

FARMER: And long enough you took for the job, Josef.

JOSEF: Long? I did it very quickly, sir. I am the best sheep shearer in the neighborhood.

FARMER: Hm! That's what you think. You may go into the poultry yard and take a goose for your pay. Don't take the fattest bird, and let me see it before you leave.

JOSEF: A goose? You promised me a calf for my work.

FARMER: A calf? Nonsense! A calf is too high a price for your work.

JOSEF: But you said you would give me a calf.

FARMER: That may be so. But now that the job is done, I can see that it is worth no more than a goose. You shall have a goose or nothing.

JOSEF: I'll have the law on you, Farmer Holtz, if I don't get the calf you promised me.

FARMER: Go to court if you like. It's your word against mine, and I, the rich Farmer Holtz, say that your work is not worth a calf.

JOSEF: We shall see what the Judge says about that. An agreement is an agreement, whether a rich man or a poor man makes it.

MUSIC: (*Bridge*)

NARRATOR: The next day Josef, the shepherd, and Farmer Holtz stood before the Judge in the little town, and each told his side of the story. The shepherd said that the farmer had promised him a calf for his work, while the farmer declared that a calf was too high a price for the work. The Judge, who was young and had not been a judge very long, scratched his head and looked very puzzled. (*Fade*) At last he said,

JUDGE: Each of you seems to be right about this. The farmer made a promise to you, Josef, which he should keep.

JOSEF: I knew you would see that I got justice, your Honor.

JUDGE: On the other hand, perhaps a calf is too high a price for Farmer Holtz to pay for that work.

FARMER: I knew you would see it my way, your Honor. The shepherd asks too much.

JUDGE: It's a difficult case to decide. I'll tell you what I'll do. It may be that one or the other of you did not understand what he was saying at the time the agreement was made. I shall try to find out which of you has the better brains. I'll set you a riddle to answer. The man who gives the better answer shall keep the calf.

JOSEF: But, your Honor! I want only justice. I am only a simple shepherd, not a guesser of hard riddles such as a judge would ask.

FARMER: Let's hear the riddle, your Honor. I got rich through using my brains.

JUDGE: You must tell me three things. One, what is the swiftest thing on earth? Two, what is the sweetest thing on earth? Three, what is the richest thing on earth? The man who gives me the best answers to these three questions keeps the calf.

Come back here tomorrow morning, and be ready to answer my three questions.

SOUND: (*Pounding of gavel*)

JUDGE: Next case!

MUSIC: (*Bridge*)

NARRATOR: The rich farmer went home from court and asked his wife to help him with the best answers to the Judge's riddle. The shepherd asked his daughter Manka what she thought the best answers were. The next day (*Fade*) the rich farmer and the poor shepherd appeared before the Judge again.

JUDGE: Well, I see you are both back again. Are you ready with the answers to my questions?

FARMER: I am ready, your Honor.

JOSEF: I hope I have the answers your Honor will like.

JUDGE: Very well, then. Farmer Holtz, I shall give you the chance to answer first. What is the swiftest thing on earth?

FARMER: My wife says our mare is the swiftest thing on earth.

JUDGE: And what is the sweetest thing on earth?

FARMER: Why, honey, says my wife.

JUDGE: And lastly, what is the richest thing on earth?

FARMER: I say there is nothing richer than to have a chest full of gold pieces.

JUDGE: All well answered, Farmer Holtz. But to be fair, we must ask the shepherd his answers to these questions. Well, Josef, what is the swiftest thing on earth?

JOSEF: The swiftest thing on earth, your Honor, is thought, because thought travels faster than the eye can see.

JUDGE: Good! And what is the sweetest thing on earth?

JOSEF: Sleep, your Honor. Nothing is sweeter than sleep when a man is tired.

JUDGE: Better yet, Josef! And now, the last question. What is the richest thing on earth?

JOSEF: The richest thing on earth, your Honor, is the earth itself, for out of the earth come all the riches of the world.

JUDGE: Wonderful, Josef! Good for you! Those are the cleverest answers I have ever heard in this court. The farmer's calf is yours, and well-earned it is.

JOSEF: Thank you, Judge.

JUDGE: But tell me, Josef. You appear to be a simple, uneducated shepherd. Did you think out these answers by yourself?

JOSEF: No, your Honor. My daughter Manka told me what to say.

JUDGE: She must be a very clever girl, that daughter of yours. I should like to test her cleverness further.

JOSEF: In what way, your Honor?

JUDGE: I should like to give her a little task to do, just to see how she would go about it.

JOSEF: I'm sure she won't mind, your Honor. But ——

JUDGE: But what, Josef?

JOSEF: The calf that you have just awarded me — is the calf still mine, no matter how Manka performs the task you give her?

JUDGE: Oh, yes. The calf is yours. You have won that fairly. Now! Here is a basket containing ten eggs that a farmer brought me this morning. Take these eggs to your daughter Manka. Tell her to have them hatched by tomorrow morning and to bring them to me.

JOSEF: But, your Honor! Chicks can't be hatched overnight. It takes three weeks for eggs to hatch.

JUDGE: A stupid hen can hatch eggs in three weeks. I want to see if your daughter is clever enough to do it in twenty-four hours. Go now, Josef. We'll see what answer your Manka can give to this.

MUSIC: (*Bridge*)

NARRATOR: In the morning the shepherd Josef was back in the Judge's courtroom. The Judge could see that Josef had brought no chicks with him, (*Fade*) so he smiled and said,

JUDGE: Well, Josef, where are the chicks that your daughter Manka was supposed to hatch overnight?

JOSEF: Manka did not hatch those eggs, your Honor.

JUDGE: Aha! Then she is not such a clever girl, after all!

JOSEF: Oh, yes, she is, your Honor. She told me to tell you that she would hatch those chicks overnight if you would first do something that she asked.

JUDGE: And what does she want me to do?

JOSEF: She gave me this handful of wheat, your Honor — I have it here in my pocket — and she said, "Tell the Judge to plant this wheat, and to see that it grows up tall and ripens, and then to have it cut down and the new grains of wheat removed from the straw — all by tomorrow morning. If he can do all this overnight, then I'll hatch the eggs overnight, and I'll bring the chicks to eat the new wheat he has grown and harvested."

JUDGE: (*Hearty laugh*) Well! Well! A very clever answer I must say! Manka is indeed a clever girl.

JOSEF: I have always thought so, your Honor.

JUDGE: She is so clever that I should like to marry her. Have you any objections to me as your son-in-law?

JOSEF: My daughter marry a judge? That would indeed be an honor for me, and a fine thing for her. A fine thing for you, too, if I may say so, your Honor. Manka is as pretty as she is clever, and you have seen how clever she is. She will make a good wife for a wise, handsome young man like you.

JUDGE: Yes, I have seen your daughter several times, though I have never spoken to her, and I do believe she is the prettiest girl in this town. Tell her then, Josef, that I shall be very happy if she will marry me.

JOSEF: I can answer for her, your Honor. I am sure she will be happy to marry you, as long as I am willing. When would you like the wedding to take place?

JUDGE: Shall we say — well, in three weeks?

JOSEF: That will be plenty of time. Manka has her wedding chest filled with linens that she hemmed and embroidered herself, and all she needs to do now is to make her wedding dress.

JUDGE: That's agreed, then. There is just one thing more, Josef. I must be sure she is willing to obey me in everything and to do exactly what I tell her, as a good wife should.

JOSEF: Oh, Manka has always been an obedient daughter, and I am sure she will be an obedient wife, too.

JUDGE: That may be, but before I marry her I want proof of that.

JOSEF: What kind of proof, Judge?

JUDGE: Tell Manka that sometime before the wedding she must come to my house. It must be neither by day nor by night.

JOSEF: How do you mean that, your Honor? It must be some hour.

JUDGE: That is for her to think out. Also, she must come neither dressed nor undressed.

JOSEF: But how can that be, sir?

JUDGE: Furthermore, Josef, she must arrive neither riding nor walking.

JOSEF: Neither riding nor walking! But the girl has no wings! She cannot sail up into the sky and then down on your rooftop!

JUDGE: She must find a way to do what I ask or she cannot become my wife.

JOSEF: I'll tell Manka that. But I'm sure even my clever Manka will not be able to think up a way to arrive neither by day nor by night, neither dressed nor undressed, neither riding nor walking. The riddle, your Honor, is too deep for me.

JUDGE: Go now, Josef, and tell Manka what I want. She must find a way to do it, or I will not marry her.

MUSIC: (*Bridge*)

NARRATOR: The shepherd went home, shaking his head sadly as he thought over the latest riddle that the Judge had set his daughter. (*Fade*) When Josef came into the house, Manka said,

MANKA: Well, Father, did you give the Judge the handful of grain I sent him?

JOSEF: Yes, Manka.

MANKA: (*Laughs*) And was he willing to plant and harvest the wheat, and feed it to my chicks tomorrow morning?

JOSEF: He said you were a very clever girl.

MANKA: Did he really say that, Father?

JOSEF: Yes, and he said that you were so clever that he'd like to marry you. Would that please you, Manka?

MANKA: Oh! That would certainly please me. I have seen the Judge, and he is very handsome. What did you say to him, Father?

JOSEF: I said you were as pretty as you were clever and would be a good wife for him.

MANKA: That is certainly good news, Father. What is it, then, that makes you look so puzzled and almost sad?

JOSEF: The Judge wants to be sure you will be an obedient wife, so he has asked you to do something that you could never do. He has given you another riddle.

MANKA: What is the riddle this time?

JOSEF: He wants you to come to him sometime before the wedding, but you must arrive neither by day nor by night, neither dressed nor undressed, neither riding nor walking. How can anybody do that?

MANKA: Don't you worry, Father. I'll find a way of carrying out that riddle. You'll be the Judge's father-in-law, no matter how many riddles he may think up.

MUSIC: (*Bridge*)

NARRATOR: About a week later the Judge was wakened from a sound sleep by a loud knocking at the door of his house. He jumped out of bed, threw a coat over his shoulders, and stuck his head out of the window.

JUDGE: Who's knocking? Who's there?

MANKA: It's I, Manka, your Honor.

JUDGE: Who?

MANKA: It's Manka, the shepherd's daughter, soon to be your wife.

JUDGE: What are you doing here at this time?

MANKA: You asked me to come.

JUDGE: I asked you to come at this hour? Wait a second till I rub the sleep out of my eyes. I can hardly see in this half light. Are you sure you're Manka?

MANKA: Of course, Judge. Who else would be coming at this hour?

JUDGE: But Manka is too clever a girl to be awake and out at this time. Why, it's barely dawn.

MANKA: If you are wide awake now, Judge, you will remember that you asked me to come to you neither by day nor by night.

JUDGE: And it is dawn now, the time when night has gone and day has not yet come. By Heaven, Manka, you really have arrived when it is neither day nor night!

MANKA: Then I have obeyed you in that part of your command.

JUDGE: But I ordered that you should come neither dressed nor undressed and you are certainly dressed. That part of my command you have not carried out, Manka.

MANKA: Oh, yes, I have! This is not really clothing I am wearing, and yet I am not unclothed.

JUDGE: How do you reason that out?

MANKA: This thing that covers me from neck to ankles is a large fisherman's net, wrapped neatly round and round me many times so that it looks like a dress. Yet surely you must admit that a fisherman's net is not an article of clothing. Therefore, I am neither dressed nor undressed.

JUDGE: Very well thought out, Manka! Very clever!

MANKA: Now please make sure that I have also arrived neither riding nor walking.

JUDGE: That part of my order you certainly have not carried out, Manka. I see you came here riding on a goat.

MANKA: You see the goat, but I did not ride on it.

JUDGE: Then you must have walked here.

MANKA: No, I did neither, yet the goat helped me get here.

JUDGE: Nonsense, Manka! You either walked or you rode here on this goat.

MANKA: If you will rub more sleep out of your eyes, Judge, you will see how I did what you wished. The goat is a small animal, not very high from the ground, isn't it?

JUDGE: Yes

MANKA: Well, I sat on the goat sideways. I kept my left foot up against the side of the goat, but the toes of my right foot were on the ground. I'll make the goat take a few steps, so that you will see. Get up, Billy! (*Off mike*) Now turn around, Billy! Do you see now?

JUDGE: By Heaven, Manka! You are the cleverest girl!

MANKA: And have I carried out your riddle correctly?

JUDGE: You certainly have! I never thought it could be done. I could not find such a clever girl for a wife anywhere else in the world. Will next week suit you for our marriage?

MANKA: It will suit me perfectly, Judge.

JUDGE: I'll see you later in the day, Manka. Oh! Oh! Wait a minute, Manka!

MANKA: What is it, Judge?

JUDGE: I've just had another thought.

MANKA: Another of your riddles?

JUDGE: No, I just want you to make me one promise.

MANKA: What's that?

JUDGE: Promise me that when we're married you will not interfere in my law cases. If you ever do, home you go to your father's house again.

MANKA: I'll try, if you will promise not to make up any more riddles for me to guess.

JUDGE: Agreed, Manka!

MUSIC: (*Bridge*)

NARRATOR: And so Manka and the Judge were married. Did they live happily ever after? And is this the end of their story? No, this story goes on to say that Manka really tried hard for a long while not to give her husband advice in his law cases. But one day she did interfere, (*Fade*) and her husband said to her sadly,

JUDGE: Manka, you have broken your promise. Now you must go back to your father's house.

MANKA: Do you really mean it, husband?

JUDGE: I do. It makes me unhappy to tell you so, but a promise is a promise, and you must go.

MANKA: Very well, if you wish it. I'll leave tonight.

JUDGE: When you leave, Manka, you may take with you only one thing, the one thing you love best in this house.

MANKA: I agree. But before I go, husband, will you let me cook you one more meal? I want you to remember my cooking when I'm gone.

JUDGE: Ah! Your cooking! I shall certainly miss your delicious meals. But I feel we must keep our bargain. Believe me, Manka, this makes me very sad.

MANKA: Don't worry about me, husband. Just be sure you come to the table promptly tonight.

MUSIC: (*Bridge*)

NARRATOR: Well, Manka prepared a grand feast for her husband. She cooked all the dishes he was particularly fond of, and she kept piling more and more food on his plate. He ate so much, he began to feel drowsy soon after he finished eating, and he lay down for a nap. As soon as her husband was fast asleep Manka had a servant take him to her father's house. When the Judge woke up, an hour or so later, he rubbed his eyes (*Fade*) and wondered where he was.

JUDGE: What's this? Where am I? Manka!

MANKA: Yes, husband?

JUDGE: This is not our house. Why, it's your father's house! What are we doing here?

MANKA: Rub the sleep out of your eyes, and I'll tell you. It always takes you a long time to wake up.

JUDGE: You're right, Manka. Now, tell me, what are we doing in your father's house?

MANKA: You sent me home today, because you said I had interfered in a law case of yours.

JUDGE: (*Shamed voice*) Yes. Yes, I remember. But when did I myself come here, and why?

MANKA: You said I might take with me only one thing — the one thing I loved best in our house. And so, when you were asleep, I took the thing I loved best — you, my husband.

JUDGE: Oh! (*Brief pause*) Manka, I am so ashamed of myself! How could I have ordered you to leave me! Forgive me. I did not realize I was making up another riddle for you to guess. You must come home with me now, at once, and never leave me again.

MUSIC: (*Bridge*)

NARRATOR: And so Manka and the Judge went back to their own home. After that, whenever a difficult case came up in court, the Judge used to say, "I think I had better consult my wife, Manka. She is a very clever woman." And he was always very careful never to speak in riddles to his wife again.

MUSIC: (*Up and out*)

ANNOUNCER: So at last the Judge and his wife Manka really did live happily ever after. Be sure to listen to our next story which comes from Japan. It is called *One-Inch Fellow*.

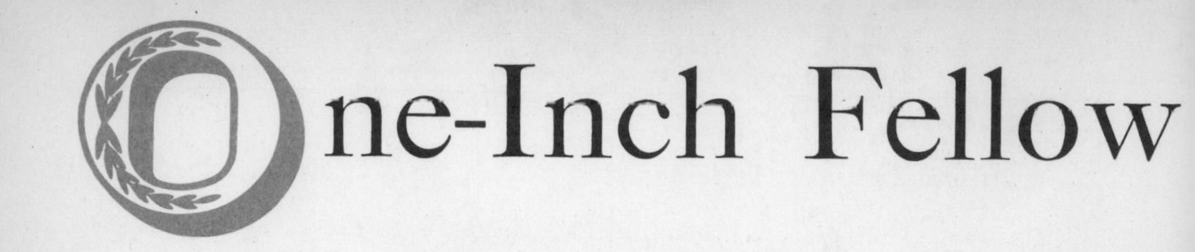

One-Inch Fellow

CAST		
	MAN	ONI
	WOMAN	LADY YO-SAN
	ONE-INCH FELLOW	ANNOUNCER
	LORD	NARRATOR

SOUNDS

Wind

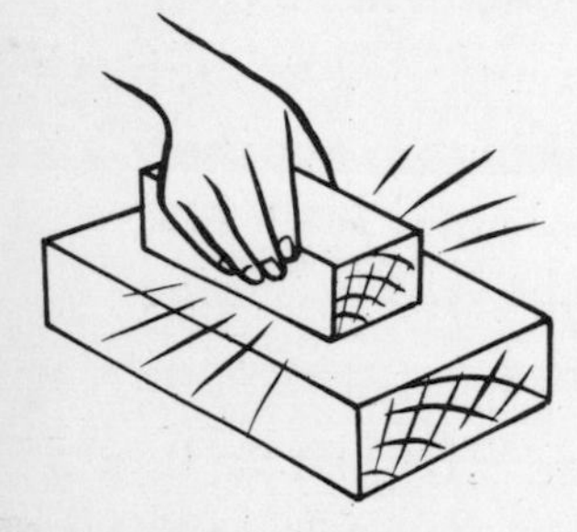

Wood against wood

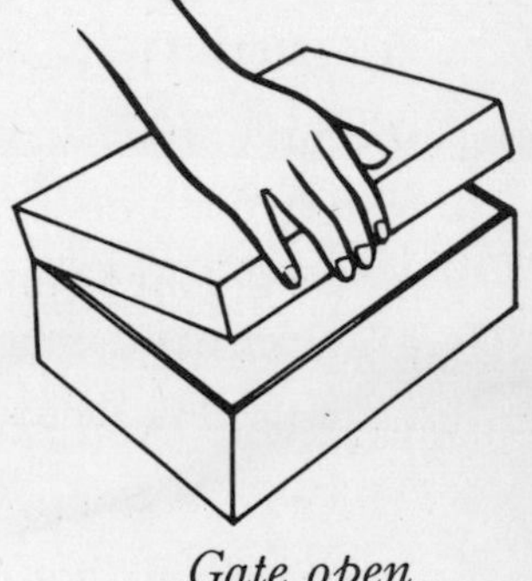

Gate open

ANNOUNCER: Hello, boys and girls! It's time for another of our *Tales from the Four Winds.* This one is called *One-Inch Fellow* and it comes from the land of Japan. Though One-Inch Fellow was very small, you will find that he was braver and brighter than people who were many times his size.

MUSIC: (*Up and out*)

NARRATOR: There once lived in Japan a man and his wife who had no children. They kept wishing for a child. One morning the woman went to the temple of the god of mercy and prayed for a long time. (*Fade*) She begged,

WOMAN: Oh, Kwannon, god of mercy, send us a little child. My husband and I will be so good to it. It does not matter whether it is a boy child or a girl child. Send us a child, please, even if it is only as small as my thumb. We will love it.

MUSIC: (*Bridge*)

NARRATOR: Late that afternoon, as the man and his wife sat just inside the open door of their house, watching the sunset, a small purple cloud appeared in the sky. (*Fade*) The husband said,

MAN: Look, wife. Isn't that a pretty cloud? I never saw a lovelier color.

WOMAN: It's a beautiful rosy purple. How fast it's moving!

MAN: It's growing bigger and bigger, and it seems to be coming nearer the earth.

WOMAN: It's moving very fast now, and it seems to be coming straight at this house!

SOUND: (*Wind in and under*)

MAN: (*Frightened*) It *is* coming right at us! How bright that cloud has grown! Cover your eyes, wife!

WOMAN: My eyes are covered.

SOUND: (*Up on wind*)

WOMAN: And this wind, too! Oh, what can it mean, husband? I'm afraid!

SOUND: (*Up full on wind and fade out*)

MAN: The wind is gone now. I'll dare to open my eyes. The cloud is gone, too.

WOMAN: It must have passed over our house. We are unharmed. The gods have been good to us, husband. What is that by the door?

MAN: It looks like a big purple flower. The wind must have blown it into the house from our garden.

WOMAN: But we have no such flowers in our garden. Why! It's a ball of soft silk. And look what's inside!

MAN: A tiny little baby! Such a beautiful little boy!

WOMAN: He's no bigger than my own thumb. Oh! That's what I prayed for this morning, husband. I prayed to Kwannon, the god of mercy, to send us a child, even if it should be no bigger than my thumb.

MAN: And the god Kwannon has sent it, in that purple cloud. (*Laugh*) Why, the little fellow is only about an inch long!

WOMAN: But he's beautiful! What shall we call him?

MAN: Let's name him for his size. We'll call him One-Inch Fellow.

WOMAN: One-Inch Fellow! You are the tiniest little baby that ever was, but, oh, how I love you, One-Inch Fellow!

MUSIC: (*Bridge*)

NARRATOR: As time went on, One-Inch Fellow proved to be a very clever boy, but he never grew any taller than he was the day he arrived. His parents took very good care of him and brought him up to be obedient, honest, and kind. When One-Inch Fellow was fifteen, he felt he was old enough to go out into the world and try to find work. (*Fade*) One morning he said to his parents,

ONE-INCH FELLOW: Honorable parents, I am now fifteen years old. You have been very good to me, and I am grateful to you for your care.

WOMAN: You have been a good son to us, One-Inch Fellow.

ONE-INCH FELLOW: Thank you, Honorable Mother. I feel that now I should find work for myself to repay you for all your kindness.

MAN: You want to work, my son?

ONE-INCH FELLOW: Yes, Honorable Father. I want to work and make a great name for myself, so that you will be proud of me.

WOMAN: But what can you do? Where will you go?

ONE-INCH FELLOW: To the big city.

WOMAN: The big city! That is so far away, down the river.

ONE-INCH FELLOW: I know that. But I want to work for a great lord, and so learn to be a great lord myself. Please give me permission to go, Honorable Parents.

MAN: Well, you are very small, but a great heart and a great mind can be in a small body. You have my permission, One-Inch Fellow.

WOMAN: And my permission, too, my son. Your father and I will miss you very much, but we know we can't keep you at home much longer. I must make you a new kimono, handsome enough for a boy in the service of a great lord.

ONE-INCH FELLOW: Thank you, Honorable Parents. I promise that I shall never make you ashamed of me, but shall make you proud and happy.

MUSIC: (*Bridge*)

NARRATOR: So One-Inch Fellow's mother made him a handsome new kimono, so that he'd be dressed in fine fashion. And his father fixed up a tiny soup bowl as a boat, with a pair of chopsticks to use as oars. His father also gave him a fine, sharp-pointed needle for a sword, in a holder made of straw.

When the day came for One-Inch Fellow to leave, his mother gave him some small rice balls and some bits of salted plum tied up in a tiny handkerchief as food for his journey to the big city. His parents both went down to the river's edge to watch him start off.

MAN: Now, my son, before I put you into your tiny soup bowl of a boat and give you the chopstick oars, I want to remind you again to be kind and trustworthy, no matter whom you meet.

ONE-INCH FELLOW: Yes, Honorable Father. I shall always remember what you have taught me.

WOMAN: (*Crying a little*) Oh, my son, I shall miss you so much! Be sure to send back a message to us as soon as you can. May no harm happen to you.

MAN: Good-bye, One-Inch Fellow! Good luck to you!

MUSIC: (*Bridge*)

NARRATOR: Little One-Inch Fellow rowed down the river in his tiny soup bowl with his chopstick oars. At last he reached the shores of the big city.

He climbed out of his soup bowl, but he left the bowl and oars in the water. (*Fade*) For, said he to himself,

ONE-INCH FELLOW: When I return to the village of my parents, I shall be a great man with many servants, so I shall not need this little boat of mine any more.

MUSIC: (*Bridge*)

NARRATOR: One-Inch Fellow walked along the streets of the big city, looking for the finest house in the city. At last he stopped at the house with the largest wall and the widest gateway. He knocked at the gate with his little sword and (*Fade*) cried out,

ONE-INCH FELLOW: Open the door! I wish to speak to the lord of the palace!

NARRATOR: The great lord of the palace, who was just inside the gate, about to go out with his many servants, heard the little voice calling through the keyhole. He ordered a servant to open the gate.

SOUND: (*Gate opened*)

NARRATOR: The great lord looked around for the speaker.

LORD: Who is it? Where is that little voice coming from?

ONE-INCH FELLOW: It is I, my lord. Look down near your feet.

LORD: Well! A tiny little man, no bigger than my daughter's thumb! (*Kindly laugh*) Well, who under the sun are you?

ONE-INCH FELLOW: I am called One-Inch Fellow, my lord, and I have come to the city to work for some great lord.

LORD: And you have picked me as your master! It pleases me greatly that a young man as handsome as you should choose me.

ONE-INCH FELLOW: Your house is the finest in the city, my lord, and I should be very happy if you will take me into your palace and let me learn the ways of great people.

LORD: You seem very sure of yourself for a young man of your size, One-Inch Fellow. Well, you can make yourself useful in many ways. Yes, I'll take you into my palace. I shall set you to watch over my daughter, the Lady Yo-San. (*Laugh*) How she will enjoy having you to guard her!

ONE-INCH FELLOW: No harm will ever come to Lady Yo-San with me to watch over her, my lord. This sword of mine shall guard her well.

LORD: Hop onto my hand, One-Inch Fellow, so that I can see that sword of yours. (*Hearty laugh*) Well! A needle in a holder of straw! A mighty sword, indeed! But you have a big heart inside that small body of yours, and that counts for as much as a strong sword. I'll take you to Lady Yo-San now.

MUSIC: (*Bridge*)

NARRATOR: At the palace of the rich lord, One-Inch Fellow soon proved himself very useful. He picked up pine needles blown into the palace, and found tiny things too small for ordinary-sized people to see. He was quick and clever and willing and always polite, so that he was well-liked by everybody. Lady Yo-San, too, thought him a brave, polite little lad, and when she went out walking One-Inch Fellow always went along, perched on the shoulder of one of her bodyguards.

One feast day Lady Yo-San started for the temple to pray to the goddess whose special day it was. Her maids and her soldiers went with her. One-Inch Fellow went along too, carried on the shoulder of a guard. As they came to the edge of a forest, they heard a loud roar and spied the oni, the giant of the forest, coming towards them.

VOICES: The oni! The terrible oni of the forest is coming! He will catch us and eat us! Run for your lives! The oni!

NARRATOR: Lady Yo-San's maids and soldiers, frightened by the roar of the oni, ran away in a great hurry. The Lady herself was so terrified that she fell to the ground in a faint. Only brave One-Inch Fellow was left on guard. He shouted up at the oni,

ONE-INCH FELLOW: Back to your forest, oni! Don't come near my lady!

ONI: Who's talking? Where does that small voice come from?

ONE-INCH FELLOW: Look down near your left foot. I am One-Inch Fellow, bodyguard to Lady Yo-San. Keep away, you wicked oni!

ONI: (*Roaring laugh*) I'll put you on my hand, so I can see you. Will you look at this little dot of a man playing guard for a lady! I'll carry Lady Yo-San off to my forest if I wish, and you won't stop me.

ONE-INCH FELLOW: You shall not touch her, you wicked oni! I'll fight you with this sword of mine.

ONI: *You'll* fight *me*, and with that little needle? Ho, ho, ho! I certainly admire your courage, little man. Very well, I'll let you fight me, and I'll eat you after I've smashed you between two of my fingers. Ho, ho! Stop tickling my cheek with that funny sword. (*Roar of pain*) Ow! My eyes! My eyes! Take that needle out of my eyes! You're blinding me! Mercy, little man! I give up! I'll leave Lady Yo-San alone.

ONE-INCH FELLOW: Put me down on the ground now, oni, and go back to your forest.

ONI: I'll put you down. But stop sticking that needle into my eyes. I'm going back to my forest. (*Fading*) My eyes! Oh, my eyes!

MUSIC: (*Bridge*)

NARRATOR: You can see what had happened. The brave One-Inch Fellow had jumped from the oni's hand to his face, and had stuck his needle sword into the oni's cheek. Now, the oni didn't mind that very much, but when One-Inch Fellow began sticking his sharp little sword into the oni's eyes, it was a different matter. The big oni howled with pain and was ready to run away without harming Lady Yo-San.

A few minutes later Lady Yo-San opened her eyes. She got to her feet and looked about her.

LADY YO-SAN: Where am I? What has happened?

ONE-INCH FELLOW: You fainted, my lady.

LADY YO-SAN: I seem to remember starting for the temple with my maids and some soldiers. Where are they all?

ONE-INCH FELLOW: We were walking along the road when the wicked oni of this forest rushed out at us. Your maids and your soldiers were frightened and feared that the oni might kill them, so they ran away.

LADY YO-SAN: The oni! Now I remember. My soldiers, who were supposed to guard me with their lives, ran away, and only you stayed with me.

ONE-INCH FELLOW: Yes, my lady. I am your special bodyguard. I could not run away from my duty. I would have given my life to protect you.

LADY YO-SAN: But what happened to the oni?

ONE-INCH FELLOW: I fought with him, my lady, and I made him run away.

LADY YO-SAN: You defeated the huge oni?

ONE-INCH FELLOW: Yes, my lady. I stuck my sword into his eyes, and forced him to beg for mercy and go back to his forest without harming you.

LADY YO-SAN: How brave and clever you are, One-Inch Fellow! My father will reward you handsomely for this brave deed of yours.

ONE-INCH FELLOW: It was my duty to protect you, my lady, and I only did my best.

LADY YO-SAN: The regular soldiers forgot their duty. Look, One-Inch Fellow, at that piece of wood on the ground. It's shaped like a large star, and it has a long handle running through the middle, almost like a hammer. Where did that come from?

ONE-INCH FELLOW: The oni had this queer-shaped hammer in his hand when he came out of the forest. He dropped it and left it behind when he ran off. Do you think it may be a magic hammer, my lady?

LADY YO-SAN: Oh, I know what that star-shaped hammer is, One-Inch Fellow. I've heard my father talk about it. That's the wishing hammer.

ONE-INCH FELLOW: The wishing hammer? What's that?

LADY YO-SAN: There's magic in it. If anybody strikes it against a tree and makes a wish at the same time, the wish will come true.

ONE-INCH FELLOW: Why not try it?

LADY YO-SAN: It looks very heavy. I wonder if I could lift it?

ONE-INCH FELLOW: If your soldiers had not run away, one of them could have helped you hold it while you made your wish.

LADY YO-SAN: Let me try. Why, it's really very light. Perhaps that's part of the magic in the hammer — that anybody can hold it.

ONE-INCH FELLOW: Then make your wish, my lady.

LADY YO-SAN: No, One-Inch Fellow. It is you who should have the wish. You have driven off the oni, and the hammer is really yours.

ONE-INCH FELLOW: Even if I were strong enough to lift the hammer, I have nothing to wish for.

LADY YO-SAN: Why not? Isn't there anything that you want to make you happy?

ONE-INCH FELLOW: I am very happy now, serving you, my lady, and the great lord, your father. Still ——

LADY YO-SAN: Then there *is* something you would wish for. What is it, One-Inch Fellow?

ONE-INCH FELLOW: I would like to be a little taller.

LADY YO-SAN: That's a wise wish to make. I'll hold the hammer for you while you put both your hands on it and make your wish.

ONE-INCH FELLOW: I hope the gods will not be angry with me for wishing that. My mother told me that Kwannon, the god of mercy, sent me down to earth in this size and shape.

LADY YO-SAN: I'm sure Kwannon will not be angry with you for wishing yourself taller. You have proved yourself a brave young man, true to your duty, and the god will be glad to reward you.

ONE-INCH FELLOW: Very well, my lady. I'll make my wish on the magic hammer.

LADY YO-SAN: I'll strike the hammer on the tree close to the ground. Put your hands on the hammer, One-Inch Fellow. Say your wish quickly as I strike.

SOUND: (*One stroke of wood against wood*)

ONE-INCH FELLOW: I wish that I shall be taller! (*Short pause*) Oh! What a queer feeling of pulling and stretching all through my body! I do feel taller! Do I look taller?

LADY YO-SAN: (*Excited*) You are five times as tall as you were before, One-Inch Fellow! I'll strike the hammer again, and you must make a second wish, to be taller yet.

SOUND: (*Two strokes of wood against wood*)

ONE-INCH FELLOW: I wish to be taller yet, much taller! (*Short pause*) Oh! Now I am half as tall as you are, my lady. Won't you strike the hammer again, so that I can wish to be as tall as a real man?

LADY YO-SAN: Gladly, One-Inch Fellow.

SOUND: (*Three strokes of wood against wood*)

ONE-INCH FELLOW: I wish to be as tall as a tall man! Oh, my lady! Now I must bend my head to look at you. Thank you for helping me!

LADY YO-SAN: How tall and handsome you are now, One-Inch Fellow! But you cannot be called One-Inch Fellow any longer.

ONE-INCH FELLOW: I, tall and handsome?

LADY YO-SAN: I'll take my mirror out of my pocket and let you see for yourself. There, look!

ONE-INCH FELLOW: Oh! I can hardly believe that this tall young man I see in the mirror is myself, the little man who was once no bigger than his mother's thumb.

LADY YO-SAN: But you are the same man, just as brave and big-hearted as you always were.

ONE-INCH FELLOW: Now that I am as tall as other men, I shall dare to speak to you as other men have done. Now I may dare to tell you, Lady Yo-San, how beautiful you are, how soft your voice, how sweet and kind you are.

LADY YO-SAN: You have learned much at the palace, One-Inch Fellow. You have learned the speech of lords and princes. But it is not fine speech alone that makes the fine gentleman. You have always been kind and thoughtful, and now you have shown true bravery as well. Let's hurry back to the palace. I want to tell my father how bravely you protected me from the wicked oni. I want him to see how strong and handsome this magic hammer has made you.

ONE-INCH FELLOW: I shall take this magic hammer with me, so that the wicked oni may not find it again and use its magic to do wicked things. Now, my lady, may I have the honor of taking you back to the palace?

NARRATOR: As you can well imagine, the great lord was surprised and delighted to see One-Inch Fellow changed into a tall, handsome young man, for the lord of the palace had grown very fond of One-Inch. After a few years One-Inch Fellow married the Lady Yo-San and sent for his parents to live with him in a palace of his own. And they all lived happily together for the rest of their lives.

MUSIC: (*Up and out*)

ANNOUNCER: And so, boys and girls, ends *One-Inch Fellow*, our tale from Japan. I'm sure you were all glad when the magic hammer made the brave little man a brave big man, so that he could marry the Lady Yo-San. Be sure to listen to our next story, *The Ugly Duckling*, that the children of Denmark like to hear.

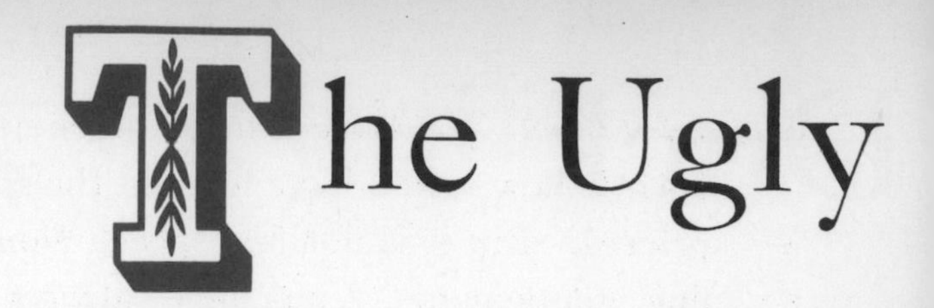

The Ugly

CAST

Mother Duck	Cat
First Duckling	Ugly Duckling
Second Duckling	Farmer
Third Duckling	Wife
Fourth Duckling	Girl
Mallard Duck	First Child
Spanish Duck	Second Child
Old Woman	Announcer
Hen	Narrator

SOUNDS

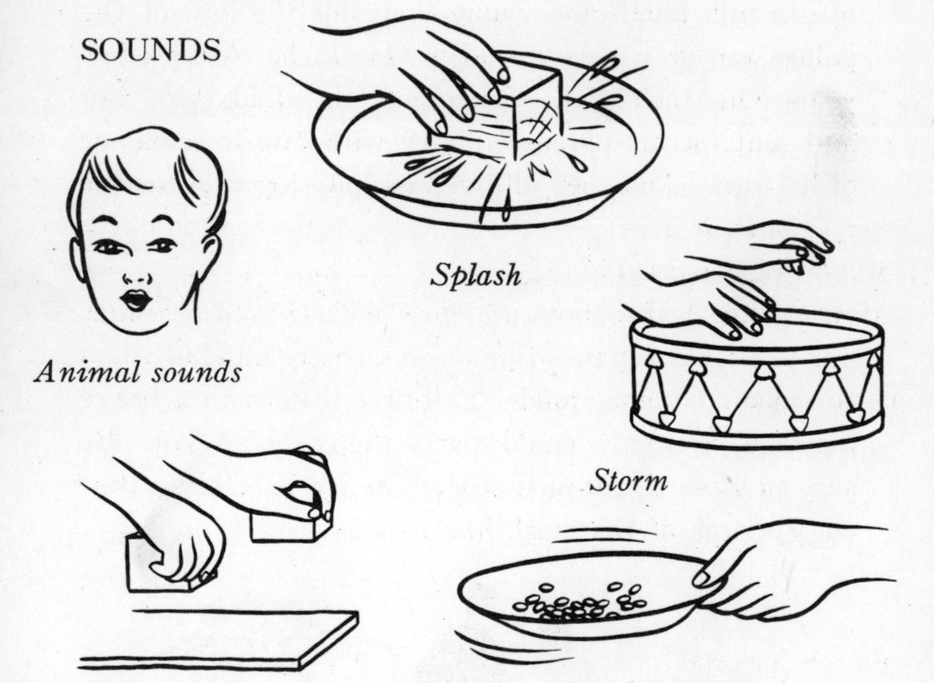

Splash

Animal sounds

Storm

Chase around room

Duckling

ANNOUNCER: Hello, boys and girls. Today we will tell you a story that comes from Denmark. The name of this story is *The Ugly Duckling.*

MUSIC: (*Up and out*)

NARRATOR: It was summer. The little farm in Denmark looked lovely. The wheatfields were yellow, the oats were green, the hay had been piled in neat stacks. All around the fields and meadows were cool green forests and deep blue lakes. The little farm was a lovely place.

That's what a mother duck thought, as she sat on her nest under a leafy bush, waiting for her eggs to hatch. She didn't mind sitting there, keeping the eggs warm, but she did wish some of the other ducks would come and quack about the doings in the poultry yard. At last one eggshell after another cracked open, (*Fade*) and out came the tiny ducklings.

SOUND: (*Peep of ducklings in and under*)

MOTHER DUCK: Oh! My little ducklings! How sweet you are, all soft and downy yellow! Look around you as much as you like. This is the world you will be living in. It's mostly a green world, and green is good for the eyes.

FIRST DUCKLING: Peep! This place is much bigger than the inside of my shell.

SECOND DUCKLING: How big this world is!

MOTHER DUCK: Quack! Quack! Do you think this spot is all the world, my darlings?

THIRD DUCKLING: How far does the world go, Mother?

MOTHER DUCK: Oh, the world reaches far across the garden and on to the next field.

FOURTH DUCKLING: And have you been all over this big world, Mother?

MOTHER DUCK: Well, no, not yet. Now, let's see. I hope you are all out of your shells. No, not all of you. The largest egg is still lying there. Oh, dear me! How much longer must I sit here just for that one egg? It is really growing very tiresome. Quack, quack!

MALLARD: Quack! Quack! I've come to quack with you a little while, Mother Duck. How are the eggs?

MOTHER DUCK: Oh, thank you, Mrs. Mallard Duck. They are all hatched except one. Aren't they the prettiest ducklings you ever saw?

MALLARD: Not bad. But you should have seen the last family of ducklings I raised. They were the best swimmers on the farm, and they had the most musical voices, just like mine. Quack! Quack!

MOTHER DUCK: I'm sure yours were lovely ducklings, too. But I can't understand why this big egg takes so long to crack.

MALLARD: Let me see that egg, Mother Duck.

MOTHER DUCK: I don't want it to get cold. I'll move aside a little, so you can see it. There.

MALLARD: Hm! That's a turkey egg, I'm sure, not a duck egg.

MOTHER DUCK: You mean the farmer fooled me and put a turkey egg into my nest for me to hatch?

MALLARD: That's what I mean. I was fooled that way once. I had a whole setting of turkey eggs put into my nest. Such a time as I had with those turkey chicks!

MOTHER DUCK: Why were they so much trouble to raise, Mrs. Mallard?

MALLARD: My dear, they were simply awful! They were afraid of the water. Imagine that! I quacked at them and quacked at them, but I simply could not get them into the duck pond.

MOTHER DUCK: Dear me! I do hope this last egg will not turn out to be a turkey egg.

MALLARD: Let me see that egg again. Yes, that's certainly a turkey egg. If you'll take my advice, you'll get off the nest. Leave that egg there, and use your time for teaching these ducklings to swim.

MOTHER DUCK: Well, I think I'll sit on it a little longer. I've been sitting here so long that a few more days won't make much difference. Besides, I'm curious to see what will come out of this egg when the shell does break.

MALLARD: Oh, very well, very well. Just as you please. If you hatch that egg and something queer comes out, don't be surprised. Quack! Quack! Quack!

MUSIC: (*Bridge*)

NARRATOR: The mother duck sat on the large egg a few days longer. At last the shell broke, and the little one crept out. (*Fade*) The mother duck looked at it and shook her head sadly.

MOTHER DUCK: Dear me! You are very large for a duckling, and you are very ugly. You don't look a bit like the other ducklings. I wonder if you really are a turkey chick, as that old duck said you'd be? Well, we'll soon find out. We'll all go down to the duck pond the first thing tomorrow morning. You will go into the water with the rest of us, even if I have to push you in.

MUSIC: (*Bridge*)

NARRATOR: The next morning the mother duck led all her little ones down to the duck pond. Splash! (*Fade*) Into the water she jumped.

MOTHER DUCK: Quack! Quack! Come, children. Jump into the water. Come, now! (*Series of light splashes*) That's fine! You all swim very well. And you, my gray ugly duckling, you are the best swimmer of them all. No, you are certainly not a turkey chick. That's enough for now, children. Come out of the water. You haven't been to the poultry yard yet. It's time I took you there and introduced you to the other ducks and the chickens and turkeys. Hop out of the pond now, all of you. Quack! Quack!

MUSIC: (*Bridge*)

NARRATOR: The mother duck led her ducklings to the poultry yard. (*Fade*) When they reached the gate she told them how to behave.

MOTHER DUCK: Be sure you walk in properly. Don't turn your toes in. A well-behaved duckling turns its toes out, so, just as I'm doing. Be polite and bow your heads to the old ducks. You must be specially polite to that very fat duck. She's a Spanish duck and the grandest duck in the yard. Now! Here we go. Watch your toes, children. Quack! Quack!

SOUND: (*Quacks, a rooster's crow, and hen's cluck*)

MALLARD: Here comes that young Mother Duck and the ducklings she's just hatched. As if there weren't enough of us in this yard already! And —— Oh! — how ugly that big duckling looks! I don't like it. I shall bite it!

MOTHER DUCK: Leave my duckling alone! It's not pretty, but it is doing no harm.

MALLARD: But it's so ugly. I don't like it. Quack! Quack!

MOTHER DUCK: I ask you, Madam Spanish Duck — you're the grandest duck in this yard — if a poor duckling should be bitten and pushed around just because it is ugly?

SPANISH DUCK: Hm! That duckling certainly is not pretty. It's a failure. I wish it could be hatched all over again.

MOTHER DUCK: That cannot be. It is not pretty, but it is very good, and it swims much better than the other ducklings. I think it will grow up very strong.

SPANISH DUCK: The other ducklings are pretty enough. Well, children, make yourselves at home. If you ever find a fish head, be sure you bring it to me. It's mine by right of being the grandest duck in the yard.

MOTHER DUCK: You are very kind, Madam Spanish Duck.

MUSIC: (*Bridge*)

NARRATOR: So the ducklings made themselves at home. But the poor ugly duckling had a very hard time of it. It was pushed about by all the other fowl in the yard. The geese hissed at it, the ducks quacked at it, the hens squawked and pecked at it, and the turkeys gobble-gobbled at it. The poor duckling didn't know where to turn. It felt sad because it was so ugly and was scolded by all the other fowl. Even its mother and brothers and sisters were often mean to it, and said,

MOTHER DUCK: Dear me! I wish I had listened to Mrs. Mallard Duck and had left you in the shell instead of hatching you.

FIRST DUCKLING: Get out of my way, you ugly thing!

SECOND DUCKLING: I wish the cat would get you, you ugly thing!

MUSIC: (*Bridge*)

NARRATOR: At last the poor ugly duckling could stand the pecking and scolding no longer. It hopped and flew over the fence and into the meadow where the wild ducks lived. For two days it lay among the reeds by the pond and drank the swamp water. On the third day a group of hunters came to the swamp, hunting wild ducks and geese. The hunting dogs splashed through the waters of the swamp, looking for the birds that had been shot down. How frightened the poor little duckling was by the noise of the guns and the sight of the hunting dogs! One of the dogs put his nose very close to the duckling, and showed his sharp teeth, then — splash! — he went on without touching it.

MUSIC: (*Up and fade under narrator's speech*)

NARRATOR: So the little ugly duckling lay quiet while the shots rattled around it. At last all was still again. But the frightened duckling lay there till dark, afraid to move. Then it hurried out of the swamp, over field and meadows, not knowing where to go. A storm arose. The wind whistled, and the rain came pouring down.

SOUND: (*Up on storm briefly and fade out*)

NARRATOR: By and by the duckling came to a tumbledown hut. The old door hung loose, partly open. The tired, wet, hungry duckling slipped through the open door into the room and hid in a dark corner.

MUSIC: (*Bridge*)

NARRATOR: The hut into which the ugly duckling had crept belonged to an old woman who lived there with her cat and her hen. The cat she called "Little Son," and "Chickabiddy Shortlegs" was her name for the hen. In the morning the duckling was discovered. (*Fade*) The hen began to cluck at it.

SOUND: (*Cluck of hen under woman's speech*)

WOMAN: What's the matter, Chickabiddy Shortlegs? Why are you clucking so angrily? That's not the way you cluck when you have laid an egg. What's wrong? I can't see very well with my old eyes. Oh, oh! Now I see. A duck has walked into our little house. It's not a big duck, as well as I can make out, but still, it's certainly a prize. Now we shall have duck's eggs. Stop clucking at it like that, Chickabiddy Shortlegs. And you, Little Son, stop curving your back and making your fur stand on end. A person would think that you two, and not I, own this house. This duck shall stay here as long as it likes. I'd better feed it, if I want it to lay eggs for me. Here, duckie, duckie, duckie!

MUSIC: (*Bridge*)

NARRATOR: Well, here the ugly duckling lived for three weeks, with the old woman, the cat, and the hen. The cat and the hen thought that they two together were half the world and the old woman the other half. So whenever the poor duckling tried to say anything, the hen and the cat would not listen. (*Fade*) They would say,

HEN: Cluck! Cluck! Who are you to talk, you ugly duckling? Can you cluck, or lay eggs, as I can?

UGLY DUCKLING: No, I can't, Chickabiddy Shortlegs.

HEN: Then you will kindly hold your tongue when I talk. Cluck! Cluck!

CAT: Meow! That's what I say, too, you ugly creature. Can you purr or meow or make your fur stand up on end as I can?

UGLY DUCKLING: No, Little Son, I can't do any of those things.

CAT: Then you will kindly keep quiet when sensible people like the hen and me are talking. Meow!

UGLY DUCKLING: Yes, Little Son. I'll go back to my corner. (*Sigh*) Oh, dear!

HEN: Cluck! Cluck! What are you sighing about now, duckling?

UGLY DUCKLING: The sun is shining in through the window, and the fresh breeze is blowing through the door. How I wish I could dive into the water and swim!

HEN: Dive into the water and swim! What can you be thinking of?

UGLY DUCKLING: It's so delightful to swim on the water.

HEN: Cluck! Cluck! Such an idea! Such a queer idea! If you would purr like the cat or lay eggs as I do, you wouldn't have such foolish wishes as to dive into the water.

UGLY DUCKLING: But it feels so good to let the water close over your head and dive down to the bottom.

HEN: Cluck! Cluck! You must have gone crazy, you duckling! Ask the cat — he's the cleverest creature, next to me — ask him if he likes to swim.

UGLY DUCKLING: Little Son, do you like to swim and dive?

CAT: Meow! Do you think I am out of my mind? Of course I don't like the water.

HEN: Cluck! Cluck! There, duckling! You might ask our mistress, the old woman. No one is as clever as she is. Do you think she has any wish to swim and dive?

UGLY DUCKLING: You've never done it, so you don't understand me.

HEN: Cluck! We don't understand you! Do you believe you are cleverer than the old woman and the cat and myself? Don't think so well of yourself, you ugly duckling.

Just be thankful that you are in a warm room with clever companions like us. It would be better if you could learn to purr or to lay eggs.

UGLY DUCKLING: I think I will go out into the wide world again.

HEN: Go ahead, you ugly creature. We won't miss you here. Cluck! Cluck!

MUSIC: (*Bridge*)

NARRATOR: So the duckling left the old house and went to live near a pond, where it swam and dived to its heart's content. Then came the autumn, with the yellow and brown leaves falling to the ground and the clouds low and gray in the sky.

One evening as the sun was setting, a flock of large handsome birds came flying out of some woods near the duckling's hiding place. They were as white as snow, and their necks were long and slender. The duckling heard their loud strange cries. It watched them spread their broad white wings and fly away. They were swans, flying to warmer countries before the cold winter came.

The duckling watched them with a strange sadness as long as it could see them. It had never thought that any birds could be so beautiful.

MUSIC: (*Bridge*)

NARRATOR: The winter grew colder and colder, and the duckling had to swim fast all the time to keep from freezing. At last one night the poor duckling lay quite still, frozen fast in the ice of the pond. Luckily a farmer, passing by very early the next morning, broke the ice (*Fade*) and took the little bird home to his family.

FARMER: Look, wife! See what I found frozen in the pond just now. Our little girl can warm it and care for it.

GIRL: Oh! A duckling! Oh, let me have it, Father! Let me play with it. Look! It's trying to move its wings.

FARMER: Here, take it, daughter.

GIRL: Oh, it got away from me!

SOUND: (*Noises of chase around room*)

FARMER: I'll catch it. The poor thing is frightened.

WIFE: Oh! It's in my milk pan! Get it out of there, quick! Shoo! Shoo! It's in the butter churn! Shoo! It's in the flour barrel! Get it out!

GIRL: I'll get it! I'll get it, Mother! Oh! It has flown out through the door. You left the door open, Father. Oh, I did want to play with it so much!

MUSIC: (*Bridge*)

NARRATOR: The poor half-frozen duckling fluttered out of the farmer's house and hid under a bush in the cold snow.

It would be too sad to tell you all that the duckling suffered in the hard winter, but at last it was spring again, and the sun shone warm and bright. All at once the duckling flapped its wings (*Fade*) and said to itself,

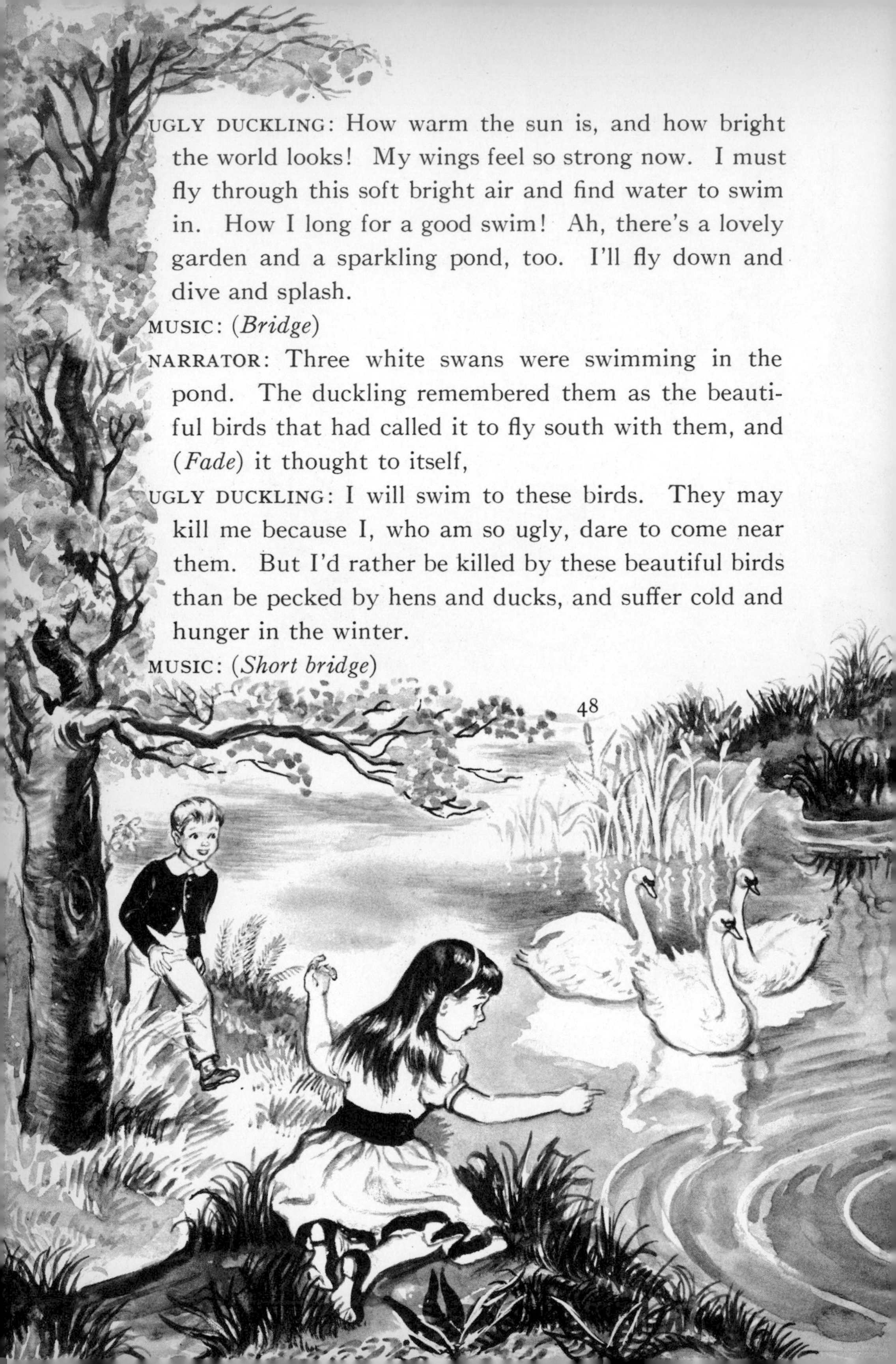

UGLY DUCKLING: How warm the sun is, and how bright the world looks! My wings feel so strong now. I must fly through this soft bright air and find water to swim in. How I long for a good swim! Ah, there's a lovely garden and a sparkling pond, too. I'll fly down and dive and splash.

MUSIC: (*Bridge*)

NARRATOR: Three white swans were swimming in the pond. The duckling remembered them as the beautiful birds that had called it to fly south with them, and (*Fade*) it thought to itself,

UGLY DUCKLING: I will swim to these birds. They may kill me because I, who am so ugly, dare to come near them. But I'd rather be killed by these beautiful birds than be pecked by hens and ducks, and suffer cold and hunger in the winter.

MUSIC: (*Short bridge*)

NARRATOR: As the duckling swam slowly towards the swans, two children came running to the edge of the pond. The younger child pointed to the duckling (*Fade*) and cried out,

FIRST CHILD: Look! There's a new swan on the pond! A young one!

SECOND CHILD: Yes, a new one has come! It's beautiful, isn't it?

FIRST CHILD: But look how it holds its head down. It seems afraid of the other swans.

SECOND CHILD: The old ones are swimming around it. They're stroking its white feathers with their beaks as if they're welcoming it. Now the young one is holding up its head. It looks very happy, doesn't it?

FIRST CHILD: It ought to be. It's so young and handsome. Oh, I do think the new swan is the most beautiful of them all! Let's run and call Mother to see it.

MUSIC: (*Bridge*)

NARRATOR: And the duckling, which saw by its reflection in the clear water that it was really a young swan, lifted its slender white neck (*Fade*) and cried joyfully,

UGLY DUCKLING: How happy I am! When I was an ugly duckling, I never dreamed of such happiness!

MUSIC: (*Up and out*)

ANNOUNCER: And so the bird which the ducks thought was just an ugly duckling grew up to be a beautiful white swan.

Be sure to listen to our next story, which comes from Spain. It is *The Three Golden Oranges*.

The Three Golden

CAST
Diego
Mother
Wise Woman
Sun Girl
Sun
Moon Girl
Narrator
Wind Girl
East Wind
First Girl
Second Girl
Third Girl
Witch
Announcer

SOUNDS

Wind
Cooing of dove

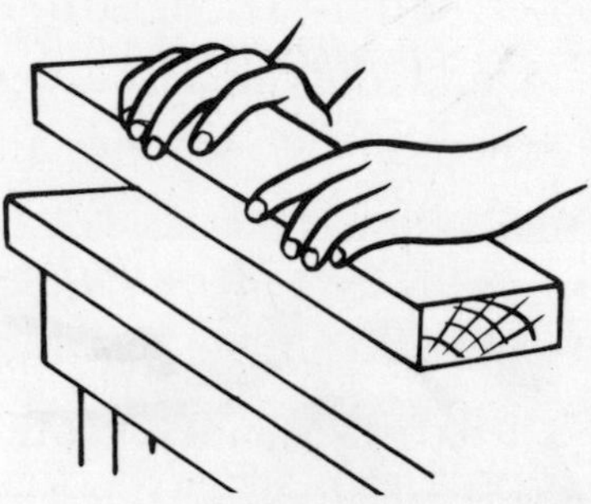

Wooden lid closed

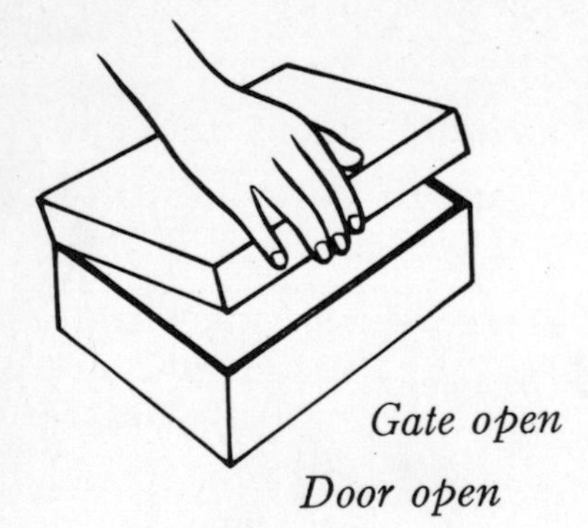

Gate open
Door open

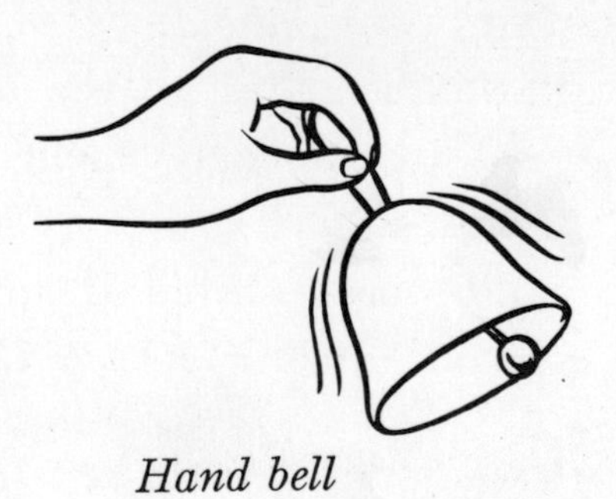

Hand bell

Oranges

ANNOUNCER: Hello, boys and girls! Today the wind blows from sunny Spain and brings you a tale of three oranges that had something strange and beautiful hidden inside them. The story is called, *The Three Golden Oranges.*

MUSIC: (*Up and out*)

NARRATOR: Once upon a time in far off Spain there lived a widow who owned a sheep ranch. She had an only son named Diego. The wool from the sheep gave them a comfortable living. On the morning of his twentieth birthday (*Fade*) Diego's mother said to him,

MOTHER: Well, Diego, my son, you are a grown young man now. I think it is high time for you to marry.

DIEGO: Yes, Mother, I agree with you. But I can't find the girl I want in any town or village around here.

MOTHER: Why not? The neighboring town of Granada is very big, and there are many girls of good family living there. What sort of girl do you want?

DIEGO: I want to marry the most beautiful girl in the world.

MOTHER: Indeed! You are a handsome lad, even if I, your mother, shouldn't tell you so. But you are not the handsomest young man in the world. Why should you have the most beautiful girl in the world as your wife?

DIEGO: All the same, Mother, I mean to marry only the most beautiful girl.

MOTHER: And where will you find her, my son?

DIEGO: I don't know. But I shall not rest until I do find her.

MOTHER: Well, Diego, if anybody can help you in your search, it is the old wise woman who lives at the foot of the hill.

DIEGO: The old wise woman! Of course! I should have thought of her at once. I'll talk to her tonight. And on my next birthday, Mother, the most beautiful girl in the world will be having breakfast with us as my wife.

MOTHER: That will be nice, indeed, if she'll have you.

MUSIC: (*Bridge*)

NARRATOR: After supper that evening Diego went down to the little house at the foot of the hill where the old wise woman lived and asked her how to find the most beautiful girl in the world. This was her advice to him.

WOMAN: You must do exactly as I tell you, Diego. Follow the road that leads into yonder snow-covered mountains, the Sierra Nevadas.

DIEGO: Yes, good lady. And what then?

WOMAN: That road will bring you to the Garden of the Three Golden Oranges.

DIEGO: But what do I want with oranges, even if they are made of gold? It's a girl I'm seeking.

WOMAN: Don't be so impatient, my lad. In that garden stands a tree, and from its branches hang three oranges that glitter like gold. If you can pluck those three golden oranges from the tree without climbing the tree, your search will be well started.

DIEGO: What? My search only started then? What shall I do with the oranges?

WOMAN: Bring the oranges to me, Diego, and I'll tell you what to do next. One of those oranges will show me who your bride will be.

DIEGO: Thank you, good lady. I'll be off at dawn tomorrow, and I'll be back with the three golden oranges tomorrow night.

WOMAN: Don't be too sure of yourself, Diego. You have a long hard way ahead of you. Be sure you follow directions, no matter who gives them to you. Go in peace now, my lad, and good luck to you.

MUSIC: (*Bridge*)

NARRATOR: At dawn the next morning Diego started along the steep road to the mountains. He walked all day. Towards evening he came to a gold-colored castle surrounded by a high wall. He rang the bell beside the gate.

SOUND: (*Hand bell*)

NARRATOR: The gate was opened by a lovely girl with hair of shining gold. Diego took off his cap and said,

DIEGO: Good evening, Señorita.

SUN GIRL: Good evening, Señor.

DIEGO: Can you tell me the way to the Garden of the Three Golden Oranges?

SUN GIRL: I do not know the way, Señor.

DIEGO: May I go in and ask your father?

SUN GIRL: (*Slightly frightened*) My father is the great Sun. He travels round the world, and he must know where it is. But you must go before he returns. He has a hot temper, and he will be angry at finding a stranger here.

DIEGO: But I must find the way to the Garden of the Three Golden Oranges. Perhaps he will not be as angry as you think. Let me stay till your father comes home.

SUN GIRL: It is not wise, Señor.

DIEGO: How lovely your hair is! There is no girl in all the town of Granada who has such lovely golden hair.

SUN GIRL: (*Pleased*) Well, you may stay. But don't blame me if Father roars at you. Come inside, Señor.

MUSIC: (*Bridge*)

NARRATOR: So Diego talked and laughed with the daughter of the Sun for a while. Suddenly the room was filled with a brilliant golden light, and there stood the great Sun, dressed all in shining yellow. He frowned at the sight of Diego, (*Fade*) and cried out,

SUN: Who is this stranger? Why did you let him in, daughter?

SUN GIRL: Oh, please don't be angry with him, Father. He means no harm.

DIEGO: If you please, Great Sun, I stopped at your castle only to ask the way to the Garden of the Three Golden Oranges. If you will tell me that, I'll be on my way at once.

SUN: No, I don't know where that is. Climb higher up the Sierras to the home of my sister, the Moon. Perhaps she can tell you. Now go quickly, young man, before I lose my temper and turn my hot beams on you.

DIEGO: I'll go at once. Thank you, Great Sun.

NARRATOR: On and up climbed Diego till by and by he came to a castle that shone like silver. He rang the bell outside the door.

SOUND: (*Hand bell*)

NARRATOR: A pretty girl with fair hair and gray eyes opened the door. Diego took off his cap and said,

DIEGO: Good evening, Señorita.

MOON GIRL: Good evening, Señor. What brings you here?

DIEGO: Can you tell me the way to the Garden of the Three Golden Oranges?

MOON GIRL: I never saw it myself, but I'll ask my mother, the Moon. She is just getting ready to start her journey through the sky. (*Loudly*) Mother! There's a young man here who wants to know how to get to the Garden of the Three Golden Oranges. (*Slight pause*) The gray castle — yes — my uncle. Perhaps. Thank you, Mother.

DIEGO: What did your mother say? And who is your uncle, Señorita?

MOON GIRL: Mother says you should keep on climbing till you come to a castle of gray rock. That's the home of my uncle, the East Wind. He blows all over the world, and he's sure to have seen the garden you are seeking.

DIEGO: Thank you kindly, Señorita. I'll be on my way.

NARRATOR: Upward and onward Diego climbed, all night long. At break of day he came to the castle of gray rock, the home of the East Wind. When he rang the bell, a very pretty girl with brown hair and brown eyes came to the door. Diego took off his cap and said,

DIEGO: Good morning, Señorita.

WIND GIRL: Good morning, Señor. What brings you here at this hour?

DIEGO: I'd like to talk to the East Wind, if you please.

WIND GIRL: My father is not at home, and that is lucky for you, young man. You had better leave at once, for if he finds you here he will blow you over the top of the Sierras.

DIEGO: Such a pretty girl as you cannot have such a terrible father.

WIND GIRL: Oh, my father is very kind to *me*, but he does not like strangers.

DIEGO: All I want is to ask him how to find the Garden of the Three Golden Oranges.

WIND GIRL: Well — if you will talk to me about the world down below these mountains, I'll hide you in the chest beside the fireplace when I hear my father coming home for breakfast. Then I'll ask him the way to the garden. You must listen to what he says, and then you must leave the castle without his seeing you.

DIEGO: Thank you, Señorita. I'll gladly tell you about the world below these mountains. It's a pretty place, (*Fade*) filled with pretty flowers, and green fields, and birds, and ——

MUSIC: (*Bridge*)

NARRATOR: And so Diego told the daughter of the East Wind about the sunny lands below the mountains. Pretty soon there was a clatter and a roaring noise in the courtyard.

SOUND: (*Wind off mike*)

NARRATOR: The air in the room grew chilly and damp. The East Wind's daughter cried out,

WIND GIRL: That's my father coming! Hide in this chest by the fireplace! Quick, before he comes into the room!

SOUND: (*Light sound of wooden lid dropped*)

WIND: (*Loud, but kindly voice fade in*) Ooooo! Well, my darling, I'm glad to be home again. I've blown half-way 'round the world today.

WIND GIRL: I'm so glad you're back, Father. I wish I could go with you on some of your journeys.

WIND: Ho! Ho! What would a pretty girl like you do, traveling with a roaring fellow like your father?

WIND GIRL: I'd like to see the world, Father. I'd like to see the — the Garden of the Three Golden Oranges. I've dreamed of it. Is there really such a place?

WIND: Oh, yes, my dear. It's the loveliest garden in the world.

WIND GIRL: And where is it?

WIND: It's just the other side of the highest peak of the Sierra Nevadas. If you should stand on that peak, you could look down on the garden and the wonderful tree that has the three golden oranges on it.

WIND GIRL: Will you take me there some day?

WIND: That's a journey for a strong young man. Stop dreaming of places a pretty girl like you could never reach. Now give me my breakfast, my pet.

WIND GIRL: Yes, Father. I have the table all set for you, with the back of your chair to the fireplace, so the fire can warm your back as you eat. I'll sit at your side and spin. The sound of the wheel will make you sleepy. Now, tell me, Father, what you saw on your travels today.

MUSIC: (*Bridge*)

NARRATOR: When his warm breakfast and the warm fire had made the East Wind fall asleep in his chair, Diego quietly crept out of the chest, thanked the girl, and slipped out through the door. He climbed up and up through deep snow all that day and most of the night. At dawn he found himself on top of the highest mountain peak. When he looked down he saw at last the Garden of the Three Golden Oranges, the loveliest garden in all the world. In the very center stood the orange tree. Even from his mountain top Diego could see the three oranges shining in the sun.

MUSIC: (*Up and out quickly*)

NARRATOR: Quickly Diego ran down the side of the mountain and through the garden hedge. The garden was silent, and not a person was in sight. Diego remembered what the wise woman had told him. He must not climb the tree to get the oranges. So he used all his strength to make one mighty jump, high enough to catch the branch, and he pulled the oranges off the tree. He put the golden-skinned fruit into his pockets and started back to Granada.

MUSIC: (*Bridge*)

NARRATOR: The way back to the town of Granada was much harder for Diego. The snow on the mountains was deep, and he was very tired from his long journey. When at last he was down from the mountains and saw the houses of the town below him, he sat down under a tree to rest. He was hot and thirsty. He took one of the golden-skinned oranges out of his pocket and looked at it longingly. He wished he could break the skin and drink the juice. He said to himself,

DIEGO: How thirsty I am, and how I would enjoy the cool juice of this orange! I have three of these golden beauties. The wise woman needs only one of them to decide who my bride will be. If I eat just one, there will still be two left. My mouth is so dry!

NARRATOR: So Diego began to break the skin of the orange. As he took the skin off, out of the orange stepped a beautiful little lady. She was only as tall as Diego's little finger, but she was very beautiful, with bright black eyes and black hair. She wore a yellow dress and golden shoes.

Lightly she sprang from Diego's palm to the ground, and then she became almost as tall as he was. He gazed at her with joy.

DIEGO: How beautiful you are, Señorita! Surely you must be the most beautiful girl in the world, the girl I have been seeking.

FIRST GIRL: Perhaps, Señor. I am hungry. Will you give me some bread, please?

DIEGO: Bread? I have none. I have eaten all that I took with me for my journey.

FIRST GIRL: Then, Señor, I must jump back into my orange skin and go back to my tree. Adios, Señor!

DIEGO: Oh, no, no! Please don't go! (*Pause*) She's gone, and the orange, too, has disappeared. That must have been the orange the wise woman needed. Ah, me! I have lost the most beautiful girl in the world!

MUSIC: (*Bridge*)

NARRATOR: Sadly Diego went on his way towards the town. But he could not help wondering about the other two oranges. He was a bright young man, too, and he had learned a lesson. He stepped into a shepherd's hut and asked for a piece of bread. Then he sat down under a tree by the roadside and broke the skin off the top of a second orange. Out of this orange stepped a tiny lady with golden hair and the bluest of blue eyes. She wore a blue dress and silver shoes. When she hopped from Diego's palm to the ground, she grew almost as tall as he was.

DIEGO: Oh! How beautiful you are, Señorita! You must surely be the girl I have been seeking, the most beautiful girl in the world.

SECOND GIRL: Perhaps, Señor. I am hungry. Will you give me a piece of bread, please?

DIEGO: With pleasure, Señorita. Here it is. I hope it will be enough for you.

SECOND GIRL: Oh, yes. One bite is all I want. And now some water, please. I am thirsty.

DIEGO: Water? I never thought of that. I haven't any water to give you.

SECOND GIRL: That is too bad, Señor. Then I must jump back into my orange and go back to my tree. Adios, Señor.

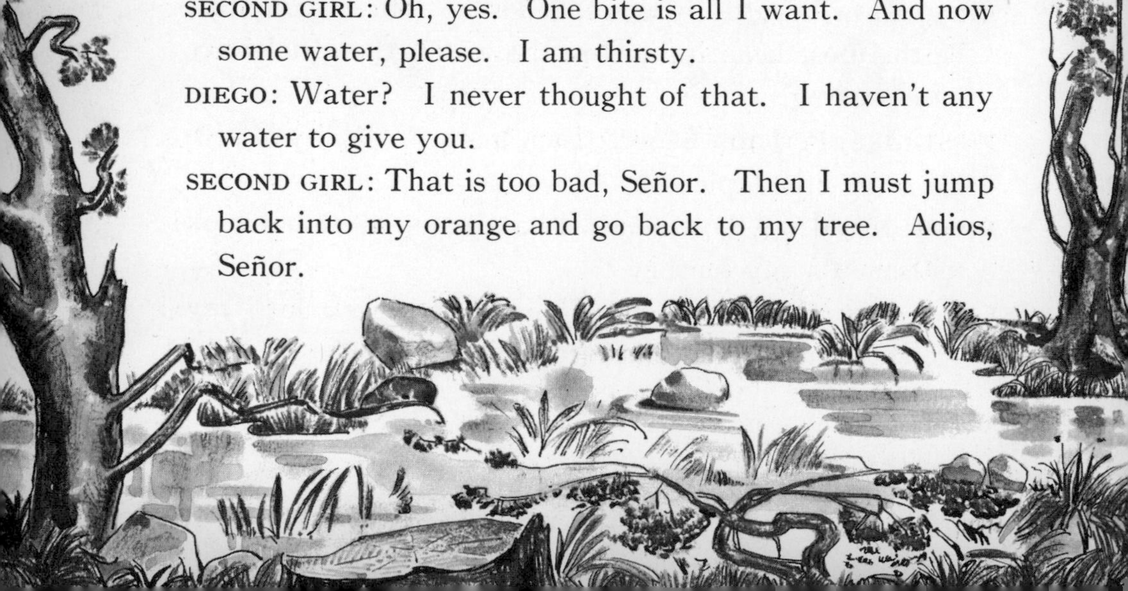

DIEGO: Oh, please don't go, Señorita! Wait here a moment, and I'll fetch you some water. (*Pause*) She's gone, and the orange has disappeared, too. Well, I must remember about water, too, for the next orange. Will there be a third girl? I wonder!

MUSIC: (*Bridge*)

NARRATOR: Well, Diego walked on down the road. This time he waited till he found a brook near the roadside before he sat down to rest and open the last of his three golden oranges. When he carefully opened the skin at the top, a beautiful girl with red-gold hair and sparkling black eyes stepped onto the palm of his hand. She wore a white dress trimmed with red, and red satin shoes. Diego gently lowered his hand, and she hopped to the ground. Then she became almost as tall as he was.

DIEGO: How beautiful you are, Señorita! This time I know that you are the girl I have been seeking. No other girl in the world could be as beautiful as you are, Señorita.

THIRD GIRL: You make very pretty speeches, Señor. But we shall see. I am hungry. Will you give me a piece of bread, please?

DIEGO: Gladly, Señorita. Here it is.

THIRD GIRL: Thank you. It looks delicious. But when I have eaten it, I shall want a drink of water.

DIEGO: When you are ready, Señorita, I will dip up some water in my cap from this brook.

THIRD GIRL: Good! You are thoughtful and will make a good husband. Now, let's eat and drink together, Señor.

DIEGO: Yes, Señorita. Then I will take you to my mother's house. She will see that I have really found the most beautiful girl in all the world for my wife.

NARRATOR: After Diego and the girl had eaten, they started for Granada. Diego looked at the beautiful girl and at her thin satin shoes, and he said,

DIEGO: I cannot bring such a beautiful bride into Granada on foot. We'll stop at the inn here at the crossroads, and I'll hire a coach for us.

THIRD GIRL: There's a pretty garden outside the inn. I'll wait there for you, Diego.

DIEGO: Sit in the shade of that tree, where it's cool.

THIRD GIRL: It will be even cooler up in the branches.

DIEGO: I'll go into the garden with you and help you up.

THIRD GIRL: Oh, I don't need any help. Now run into the inn and see about a coach for us.

MUSIC: (*Bridge*)

NARRATOR: The orange girl made herself comfortable in the lower branches of the tree and looked about her. At the foot of the tree there was a fountain. The girl bent her head and smiled at her reflection in the water. Just then an old woman came out of the inn. She was really a witch who had dressed herself as a working woman. As she leaned over to fill her pitcher from the fountain, she saw the reflection of the beautiful girl. She said,

WITCH: Ah! What a beautiful face! If I were as beautiful as that, I could marry a king and rule the world.

THIRD GIRL: (*Off mike, laughing*) How funny! You, marry a king? You look like an ugly old witch.

WITCH: Where are you? Who calls me ugly? Oh, there you are, up in the tree. So I look like an ugly old witch, do I? Well, I'll show you what an ugly old witch can do. I'm climbing up into that tree after you. I'll show you!

THIRD GIRL: (*Slightly off mike*) Oh, no, no! I'm sorry I said that! Oh! (*Fading scream, ending in coo of dove*)

MUSIC: (*Bridge*)

NARRATOR: The old witch, angry at the girl's laugh, had quickly climbed into the tree and had stuck a magic pin into the side of the girl's head, just behind her right ear. At once the girl was changed into a little gray dove that cooed sadly. A few minutes later Diego came out of the inn. He looked up into the tree and all around the garden, but he could not see the orange girl anywhere. (*Fade*) Diego called and called.

DIEGO: My love! Where are you, my dear? Come out from your hiding place. Where are you, my dear?

SOUND: (*Repeated cooing of dove*)

NARRATOR: But all that Diego heard was the cooing of the dove as the bird followed him about. Diego held out his hand, and the bird came and perched on it.

DIEGO: Come with me, pretty bird, to ask the old wise woman how I can find my lost love again.

MUSIC: (*Bridge*)

NARRATOR: Then Diego, with the dove perched on his shoulder, went to the old wise woman. She remembered him and why he had come to her before.

WOMAN: Ah, you are back, Diego. And did you find the Garden of the Three Golden Oranges?

DIEGO: Yes, I did, kind lady, thanks to your help in setting me on the right road.

WOMAN: Have you brought back the golden oranges?

DIEGO: No. I opened all three before I reached Granada.

WOMAN: Ah, Diego, that you should not have done! And what did you find in them?

DIEGO: A beautiful girl in each one. The first two disappeared almost at once. But the third one I was bringing home to be my wife, until ——

WOMAN: Until what happened?

DIEGO: I left her in the garden of the inn for a few minutes, and when I came out, she, too, had disappeared.

WOMAN: That was your punishment for disobeying me. Now you have lost your chance to marry the most beautiful girl in the world.

DIEGO: I am sorry that I disobeyed you. Please help me find my beautiful girl again, kind lady!

SOUND: (*Cooing of dove*)

WOMAN: That dove on your shoulder! Come to me, pretty little dove.

SOUND: (*Coo of dove*)

WOMAN: Ah! Just as I thought! A witch has been at your beautiful girl.

DIEGO: A witch? I remember now! There was an old woman in the garden of the inn, but I never thought she might be a witch. Can't you undo her wicked work?

SOUND: (*Cooing of dove under*)

WOMAN: Let me feel under the feathers of the dove. Nothing under the wings. Ah! Here it is, just behind the right ear.

SOUND: (*Loud cooing*)

WOMAN: This pin. I'll pull it out gently. There!

SOUND: (*Long coo*)

WOMAN: Here is your lovely girl again, Diego.

THIRD GIRL: Oh, Diego!

DIEGO: How glad I am to see you again! I was afraid I had lost you.

THIRD GIRL: You did not know me as a dove, and I could not make you understand me. I should not have laughed at the witch.

DIEGO: We both have this kind, wise woman to thank for changing you back to your own shape.

THIRD GIRL: I can never thank you enough, kind lady.

WOMAN: It is always wise to mind your manners, no matter to whom you talk.

DIEGO: And now, my dear, we will go up the path to my mother's house. She will see that I have truly brought home the most beautiful girl in all the world for my wife.

MUSIC: (*Up and out*)

ANNOUNCER: And so, boys and girls, ends *The Three Golden Oranges*, our story from Spain. I'm sure you believe that Diego deserved his beautiful wife after all his trouble in finding her.

Be sure to listen next time, when we'll tell you *The Feast of Lanterns*, a story told to the children of China.

The Feast of

CAST

Wang Chih
Wife
Ho Seen Ko
Han Chung
First Chess Player
Second Chess Player
Rabbit
Old Woman
Announcer
Narrator

SOUNDS

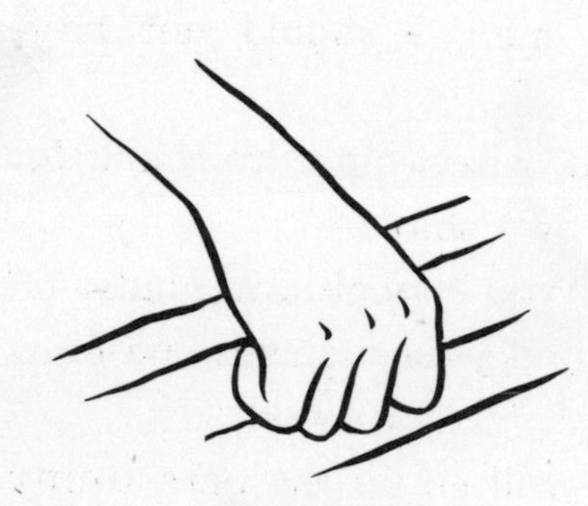

Knock

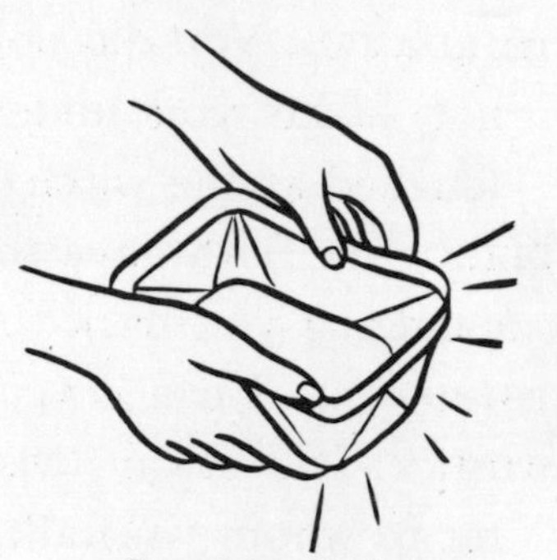

Crackle of fire

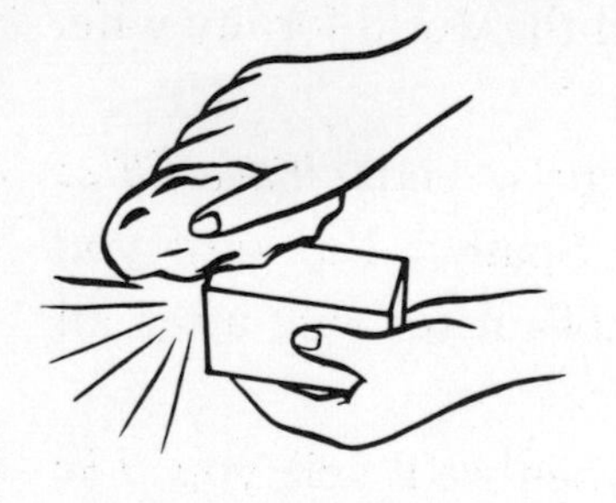

Steel against stone

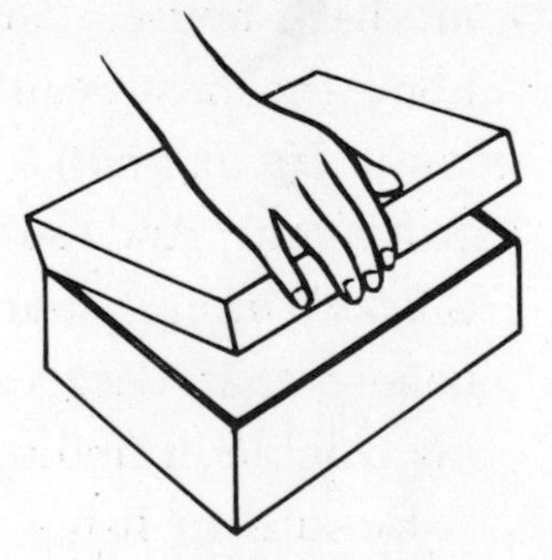

Door open and shut

Lanterns

ANNOUNCER: Hello, boys and girls. It's story time again. Today you will hear a story that comes all the way from China. It is called *The Feast of Lanterns.*

MUSIC: (*Up and out*)

NARRATOR: There once lived in China a man named Wang Chih. Though he was poor and had to work hard, he was seldom sad, for he had a cheerful wife and two happy children. One day as he was starting out for work, (*Fade*) his wife said to him,

WIFE: When you come home tonight, Wang Chih, bring some firewood back with you.

WANG CHIH: Well, I shall have to get the wood during my lunch time, wife. I'll have to climb the side of the mountain for it, and I don't like to do that in the dark.

WIFE: Get your father his axe, Han Chung.

HAN CHUNG: Yes, Mother.

HO SEEN KO: You'll be sure to come home early tonight, Father, won't you?

WANG CHIH: (*Teasing*) Why? What's going to happen tonight, Ho Seen Ko?

HO SEEN KO: As if you didn't know! It's the Feast of Lanterns. We've been talking about it for a month.

HAN CHUNG: Here's your axe, Father. I'm going to carry my big red lantern in the children's parade tonight.

HO SEEN KO: My lantern is shaped like a fish, red and black and yellow. It will look lovely with a lighted candle inside.

HAN CHUNG: Don't work too late, Father. We want you to light our lanterns for us.

WANG CHIH: I'll be home in plenty of time, children. Good-bye now, and be good children.

CHILDREN: Good-bye, Father!

WIFE: Don't forget the firewood, Wang.

NARRATOR: At noon Wang Chih did not take time to eat his lunch, but went up the side of the mountain to find firewood. He walked and walked and at last saw a small tree growing near the mouth of a cave. Before starting to chop at the tree he thought he had better look into the cave to make sure there was no wild animal hidden there. He was more than surprised to see two old men with long white beards sitting inside, silently playing chess. (*Fade*) They did not look up as Wang spoke to them.

WANG CHIH: Good morning, gentlemen. Do you mind if I watch you? I'll sit down on the ground here beside you. I know a little about chess myself. Ah! A clever move, sir! What, sir? Oh, you're waving at me to help myself to one of these dates? Thank you. I will. Mmm! They're delicious, soft and sweet. I could go on eating them forever.

MUSIC: (*Bridge*)

NARRATOR: So Wang Chih sat on the ground between the two old chess players and watched their game. They played silently, now and then reaching for one of the dates which lay on a stone beside them. Wang, too, ate the dates. He had been hungry when he went into the cave, for he had not eaten his lunch, but after a few dates he felt refreshed and no longer hungry or thirsty. By and by Wang Chih noticed something strange, (*Fade*) and he mentioned it to the chess players.

WANG CHIH: Will you pardon my interrupting your game, good sirs, to ask a question? I have noticed something which makes me wonder.

FIRST CHESS PLAYER: If you must interrupt us, ask your question quickly, young man.

WANG CHIH: My wife would smile to hear you call me a young man.

SECOND CHESS PLAYER: You are centuries younger than we are, young man.

WANG CHIH: (*Laugh*) Centuries! I see you like your little joke, sir.

FIRST CHESS PLAYER: (*Sternly*) We never joke. What did you want to ask of us?

WANG CHIH: Well, it's about your beards.

SECOND CHESS PLAYER: What about our beards?

WANG CHIH: Well, they seem to have grown so much longer since I came into the cave. Why, they are sweeping the ground now. I'm wondering if that is really so, or if I am only imagining that they have grown while I've watched your game. I mean, perhaps you had your beards hidden inside your coats and they gradually worked out.

FIRST CHESS PLAYER: No, young man, you are not imagining it. Our beards have really grown since you have been in the cave.

WANG CHIH: That is remarkable! I have never seen a beard grow so quickly.

SECOND CHESS PLAYER: Our beards have not grown particularly fast, young man.

FIRST CHESS PLAYER: How long do you think you have been in this cave?

WANG CHIH: Oh, about half an hour, I should think.

FIRST CHESS PLAYER: (*Cackling laugh*) Now it is you who are joking. Touch your axe, young man.

WANG CHIH: Why, it's all rusty! It's crumbling to dust!

SECOND CHESS PLAYER: Yes, your axe has rusted away while you sat here. Would that happen in half an hour?

WANG CHIH: I don't understand it at all.

FIRST CHESS PLAYER: Half an hour, half a century, or half a thousand years; it's all alike to the man who eats these dates.

WANG CHIH: (*Horrified*) You mean I have been here more than fifty years? But that can't be! I'm sure I came here only this noon when I stopped for lunch.

SECOND CHESS PLAYER: Go down the mountain, young man. Go back to your village and see what has happened since you left it.

NARRATOR: You may be sure Wang went down the mountain as quickly as he could. To his surprise, streets had been made and houses built in the fields where he once had worked. He looked in vain for his own little cottage and his wife and children. The people on the streets were all strangers. Even their clothes seemed strange. (*Fade*) Everywhere he went he kept asking,

WANG CHIH: Have you seen Wang Chih's wife and children? (*Fade*) Have you seen Wang Chih's wife and children?

NARRATOR: The people shook their heads and looked at him queerly when he asked them that question. At last one old woman tapped her forehead (*Fade*) and said,

WOMAN: Wang Chih! I remember that name. When I was a little girl, my grandmother told me that when she was a little girl the evil spirit of the mountain had carried off a young man by the name of Wang Chih on the evening of the Feast of Lanterns. His wife and children were left with no rice in the house.

WANG CHIH: I am that man, Wang Chih, old woman.

WOMAN: I am talking of what happened more than a hundred years ago, old man.

WANG CHIH: Old man! I, an old man?

WOMAN: Your mind must be wandering, as my mind sometimes does.

WANG CHIH: But I can't believe it!

WOMAN: Tonight is the Feast of Lanterns. If you will wait until the procession of children carrying their lanterns passes tonight, you will see two children dressed as Wang's children, Ho Seen Ko and Han Chung. Instead of lanterns, they carry an empty rice bowl to remind us that we must take care of the fatherless and the widows.

WANG CHIH: Thank you, good woman. The widow and the fatherless! My dear wife and children! I must watch the procession of the Feast of Lanterns. The old chess players and this old woman may still be wrong! Pray Heaven they are wrong!

MUSIC: (*Bridge*)

NARRATOR: With a sad heart Wang Chih watched the procession of children carrying their gay lanterns. His own children were not there. He saw only an unknown woman and two children about the ages of Ho Seen Ko and Han Chung walking beside her. All three of them carried empty rice bowls. Wang Chih walked sadly back towards the mountain. Early the next morning he again entered the cave of the old chess players. (*Fade*) With tears in his eyes he said to them,

WANG CHIH: Please, good sirs, tell me how I can find my wife and children. I cannot bear the thought that I shall never see them again.

FIRST CHESS PLAYER: Go away, young man. You are interrupting our game again.

WANG CHIH: I do not wish to be rude, sir, but I will not go away until you tell me how to find my family. I'm sure you know how it can be done.

SECOND CHESS PLAYER: If we tell you, will you go and never come here to disturb us again?

WANG CHIH: Yes! Yes! I'll never bother you again if you will help me.

FIRST CHESS PLAYER: Go to the White Rabbit of the Moon. Ask him for a bottle of the magic water of life.

WANG CHIH: And what shall I do with the magic water of life?

FIRST CHESS PLAYER: Drink it, and you will live forever.

WANG CHIH: But I don't want to live forever. I want to go back and live at the time my wife and children were living with me.

SECOND CHESS PLAYER: In that case, you must mix the magic water of life with some water out of the Sky Dragon's mouth.

WANG CHIH: The Sky Dragon! Where can he be found?

SECOND CHESS PLAYER: In the sky, naturally. He lives in a cave made of clouds.

WANG CHIH: And how can I get the water from the Sky Dragon's mouth, old man?

SECOND CHESS PLAYER: You ask so many questions! When the Dragon comes out of his cave, sometimes he breathes fire and sometimes he breathes out water.

WANG CHIH: Oh, dear me!

FIRST CHESS PLAYER: If the Dragon breathes out fire, you will be burned to ashes. If he breathes out water, you can catch it in a bottle. Now go, and leave us to our chess. (*Slight pause*) What are you waiting for?

WANG CHIH: If you please, good sirs, I should like a pair of wings to carry me through the air and a bottle to hold the water from the Sky Dragon's mouth.

SECOND CHESS PLAYER: To get rid of you, I suppose we'll have to give you what you want. Take that bottle by the pile of dates. If you will go outside, you will see a white crane flying towards you. Get on its back, and it will carry you wherever you want to go. Now leave us to our game.

NARRATOR: Well, Wang decided he would get the water from the Sky Dragon's mouth before asking the White Rabbit of the Moon for the magic water of life. So he told the white crane to take him to the cloud cave where the Sky Dragon lived. When he got there, Wang sat down before the mouth of the cave and wondered how he could get the Dragon out, and get him out breathing water, not fire. Pretty soon he had an idea. He clapped his hands with joy, (*Fade*) and told his idea to the white crane.

WANG CHIH: I know how I can get the Sky Dragon to come out breathing water, my good bird. I'll set fire to the grass outside his cave. The Dragon will see the smoke and hear the flames crackling, and he'll come out to put out the fire. He'll have to breathe water on it, and when he does, that will be my chance to collect some of that water. I'll strike my flint now and start my fire.

SOUND: (*Steel against stone, crackle of fire*)

NARRATOR: And that's exactly what Wang did, and what the Sky Dragon did. The smoke drifted into the cave, and the Sky Dragon rushed out, breathing heavy streams of water. Quickly Wang filled his bottle with this water, and was off again on the crane's back. This time he was bound for the home of the White Rabbit of the Moon, who had the magic water of life. When he came to the White Rabbit's house (*Fade*) he knocked at the door politely.

SOUND: (*Knock at door*)

RABBIT: (*Off mike*) Come in, Wang Chih.

SOUND: (*Door open*)

WANG CHIH: Good morning, White Rabbit of the Moon.

SOUND: (*Door shut*)

WANG CHIH: How did you know it was I knocking at the door?

RABBIT: Oh, I have lived thousands of years, and I have ways of learning things.

WANG CHIH: In that case, you must know why I have come here.

RABBIT: You want to live in the time when your wife and children were living with you, don't you, Wang?

WANG CHIH: Yes, White Rabbit of the Moon. Please help me find them again!

RABBIT: I want to make sure you really want to go back to them. Look through this window. What do you see?

WANG CHIH: (*Slowly*) I see streets and houses and people, many people. It is a big city. The people are not dressed in the clothes my family and I used to wear. Oh! That's the city where I was yesterday, when I watched the Feast of Lanterns. It is my old village but grown to many times its old size.

RABBIT: Now tell me, Wang. Do you want to go down to that city to live?

WANG CHIH: No, no! I don't want that! I don't know any of those people. Worst of all, my dear wife and children are not there.

RABBIT: Then come away from that window. It is the Window of the Present. Now, look down through this other window, the Window of the Past. What do you see there, Wang?

WANG CHIH: (*Happy voice*) Oh! That's my village! And that's my own little cottage! I see my dear wife and children! My wife is hanging the lanterns outside our door, and she and the children are looking towards the mountain, as if they are looking for me to come home. Please, good White Rabbit of the Moon, let me go back and live with them again!

RABBIT: You shall do so. You have the water from the Sky Dragon's mouth, haven't you?

WANG CHIH: Yes. Here it is in this bottle.

RABBIT: Ah! I'll put in a few drops of my magic water of life carefully, so! Now, drink all the water in the bottle, Wang Chih. Then you will be able to live again in the Past, as you wish.

WANG CHIH: I'll drink it gladly. (*Slight pause*) Now, how do I get down to my own village?

RABBIT: By these stairs at the Window of the Past.

WANG CHIH: Stairs? I didn't notice them before. Why, they lead right down to the road in front of my little cottage! Good-bye, White Rabbit of the Moon, (*Fade*) and thank you for all your kindness.

MUSIC: (*Bridge*)

NARRATOR: The stairs from the window of the White Rabbit's house brought Wang quickly to the road in front of his cottage. His wife was just starting to hang up the second lantern at the door. (*Fade*) She turned when she heard the children cry out.

HO SEEN KO: Oh! There's Father! Father's come home!

HAN CHUNG: Oh, Father! You said you'd try to come home early tonight.

WIFE: Well, Wang Chih! Where have you been?

WANG CHIH: I'm very sorry that I'm late. I was delayed on the mountain unexpectedly.

WIFE: And where's the firewood I asked you to bring back?

WANG CHIH: Oh! I forgot all about the firewood! The chess game drove it out of my mind.

WIFE: So that's what has made you so late, playing chess!

WANG CHIH: (*Quickly*) I'm sorry. I'll go out and get some firewood for you this minute.

WIFE: Don't bother about it now. I found a large pile of wood behind the house a little while ago. I can't imagine who could have left it there.

WANG CHIH: Perhaps it was the White Rabbit.

WIFE: Wang Chih, you were asleep and dreaming somewhere, I'm sure. Well, whoever left the wood was very kind. Now, Wang, light these lanterns at the door.

HO SEEN KO: Anyhow, Father, we're glad you came home in time to light our lanterns. They will look lovely when we march in the parade tonight.

WANG CHIH: And no one will be as happy as I shall be to stand with your mother and watch you march by.

NARRATOR: So Wang Chih stood with great happiness in his heart as his children marched in the procession of the Feast of Lanterns. But he never told his family of his adventures in the mountain cave or with the Sky Dragon and the White Rabbit of the Moon.

MUSIC: (*Up and out*)

ANNOUNCER: Weren't you happy to know that Wang Chih found his family again? I don't believe he ever went near that cave on the mountainside again, do you?

Be sure to listen to our next story, which is called *The Crowded House*. It comes from Romania.

The Crowded

CAST Judge
Peter
Anna
Announcer
Narrator

SOUNDS

Animal sounds

ANNOUNCER: Down in the southeastern corner of Europe is the little country of Romania. Travelers from eastern countries, such as Turkey, often went through Romania on their way to western lands, and travelers from the west sometimes passed through this country on their way east. Naturally it happened that some of these travelers liked the land, and decided to stay and make their homes there. That's why you will find in Romania tales that may have been brought from other lands. The story you will hear today is one that is told in Romania. It is about a wise man and a selfish man. It is called *The Crowded House.*

MUSIC: (*Up and out*)

House

NARRATOR: In a little village there once lived a very wise man. Whenever anybody in the village or the countryside was in trouble, he always went to this wise man for help and advice. Whenever two people quarreled they always went to him to settle the matter. And so this wise man came to be called the Judge. One day Peter, a man who owned a small piece of land just outside the village, (*Fade*) went to the Judge for advice.

PETER: Good morning, Judge. May peace be with you.

JUDGE: May peace be with you, Peter. What brings you here so early in the morning?

PETER: I want your advice, Judge.

JUDGE: Gladly, my friend. What is troubling you?

PETER: You know, I have a small piece of land, not big enough to be called a farm.

JUDGE: Still, you are not poor, Peter.

PETER: Well, I'm not starving, but I'm not rich either. I have a cow and a goat, and I sell their milk. Then I have some geese, a rooster, and some hens. I sell the eggs of the geese and the hens, and sometimes, before a holiday, I sell a fat hen or a goose.

JUDGE: You are better off than some other people in the neighborhood.

PETER: But I am not rich, Judge. You know my house is just one room, not too big.

JUDGE: That should be enough for you and your good wife.

PETER: Yes, it's big enough for myself and my wife. And that brings me to my trouble. My daughter Maria, her husband Paul, and their year-old baby came to live with us last week.

JUDGE: That must be fine! It was good of you to invite them.

PETER: I? No, I didn't invite them. My wife asked them to come. My son-in-law can't make a living in his own village, so my wife asked my daughter to bring her family to stay in our house. And that brings me to my question, Judge.

JUDGE: What is your question, Peter?

PETER: My house is too small for five people. What shall I do?

JUDGE: I should think you'd be glad to help your daughter when she's in trouble.

PETER: But my house has only one room, and the baby crawls on the floor and is always getting in the way. The house is too crowded.

JUDGE: Does your wife mind the extra people?

PETER: No. She is happy to have them there all the time.

JUDGE: And does your daughter sit in a chair all day?

PETER: No. She helps my wife with the housework. Why shouldn't she help her own mother?

JUDGE: And Paul, your daughter's husband, what does he do all day?

PETER: Oh, Paul helps me in the fields. Why shouldn't he?

JUDGE: And the baby — do you like it?

PETER: Oh, the baby is a bright little thing. But he crawls all over the house and is under my feet all the time. I tell you, Judge, the house is too crowded.

JUDGE: I'll tell you what to do, Peter.

PETER: Yes, Judge?

JUDGE: You say you have a cow.

PETER: Yes. She's a good milker, too.

JUDGE: Take the cow into the house.

PETER: (*Surprised*) But, Judge! I came to you because the house is too crowded already, and you tell me to take another creature into it!

JUDGE: Did you come to me for advice, or didn't you, Peter?

PETER: Yes, Judge. I'll do as you say. Thank you. I'll send you a hen for your Sunday dinner. (*Fade*) The house is already too crowded, and you tell me ——

MUSIC: (*Bridge*)

NARRATOR: Well, Peter went home, ready to do what the Judge had told him. His cow was grazing in the field at the side of the house. Peter took hold of one of her horns and led her, mooing, to the door of the house.

SOUND: (*Moo*)

NARRATOR: Anna, his wife, busy at the fireplace, (*Fade*) came to the door when the cow mooed.

ANNA: Oh! You're home again, Peter. What is that cow doing here? Chase her back into the field.

PETER: Wait a minute, Anna. The cow is going into the house.

ANNA: Into the house! Have you gone crazy, Peter?

PETER: It is the good Judge's advice.

ANNA: To put the cow into our little house?

PETER: Yes. I asked the Judge what to do because our house is so crowded, and he said, "Take the cow in."

ANNA: I don't understand it. But if the wise Judge says so, it is the thing to do. Bring the cow in, Peter.

SOUND: (*Moo of cow*)

MUSIC: (*Bridge*)

NARRATOR: So the cow stayed in the house, sometimes standing up, sometimes wandering from one corner to the other. The baby crawled between her legs, and the grown-ups tried to keep out of her way. After a week of this, (*Fade*) Peter went back to the wise Judge.

PETER: Good morning, Judge. May peace be with you.

JUDGE: May peace be with you, Peter.

PETER: I have come to you for advice again, Judge.

JUDGE: What is troubling you now, Peter?

PETER: You remember that last week I asked you what to do because my house was too crowded with myself, my wife, my daughter, her husband, and the baby.

JUDGE: Yes, I remember. Did you do what I told you?

PETER: I did. I took the cow into the house.

JUDGE: And does the house seem less crowded now?

PETER: No, Judge. The one room is even more crowded now. The cow, the baby, and all the others are more in my way than ever.

JUDGE: Does your wife complain?

PETER: No. She's too busy. In fact, Anna says she likes it because she doesn't have to go out to the barn to milk the cow now. But I am uncomfortable, and I don't like it.

JUDGE: *You* don't like it, and *you* are uncomfortable. I see. You said you have a goat, Peter, didn't you?

PETER: Yes, I have a goat, Judge.

JUDGE: My advice to you is this, Peter. Take the goat into the house.

PETER: Take the goat into the house! But my trouble is that my house is too crowded as it is!

JUDGE: You asked for my advice, didn't you?

PETER: Yes. But, Judge, you are a wise man, and yet you tell me to take another animal into our one room.

JUDGE: Take the goat into the house, Peter.

PETER: Very well, I will. Thank you for your advice, Judge. I'll send you a goose for your Sunday dinner.

MUSIC: (*Bridge*)

NARRATOR: When Peter reached his home, he found the goat tied to a tree to keep it from wandering away. He untied the animal and led it, bleating, to the door of the house.

SOUND: (*Bleat of goat*)

NARRATOR: (*Fade*) Anna saw the animal at the door and said,

ANNA: Now! Who untied that goat, I'd like to know? Oh, you're back, Peter. Well, what did the wise Judge say?

PETER: You won't believe me, Anna.

ANNA: Why shouldn't I believe you?

PETER: The Judge said that if the house is too crowded for my comfort, I should take the goat into the house, too.

ANNA: First the cow, and now the goat?

PETER: That's what the Judge said.

ANNA: Well, if the wise Judge advised it, we'll do it.

PETER: We'll have to hold our noses with the goat inside the house.

ANNA: I won't complain. Maria and I won't have to go out to the field to milk the goat. Bring it in, Peter.

SOUND: (*Bleat of goat*)

MUSIC: (*Bridge*)

NARRATOR: With the cow and the goat inside the house, Peter found life less comfortable for himself than ever. After a week or so, (*Fade*) he went back to the Judge.

PETER: Good morning, Judge. May peace be with you.

JUDGE: May peace be with you, Peter. What is troubling you now, that you come so early in the morning?

PETER: I have followed your advice, Judge, and my house is more crowded than ever.

JUDGE: Are you still uncomfortable?

PETER: Am I still uncomfortable, you ask! During the day I have to walk around the animals all the time. I am awakened at dawn by the cow's mooing, like this — Moo! Then the goat bleats, like this — Maa! When I lie down for a nap in the morning or the afternoon, the cow comes and breathes in my face, and the goat nips my nose or my ear. I tell you, Judge, my house is entirely too crowded for my comfort.

JUDGE: Do your wife and your daughter complain of lack of room or of being uncomfortable?

PETER: No, Judge. They are too busy all day, with the housework and the animals and the baby to take care of.

JUDGE: And does Paul, your son-in-law, complain?

PETER: No. When Paul comes in from working in the fields he is too tired to notice how crowded the house is.

JUDGE: And what do you do all day, Peter?

PETER: I, Judge? Well, I try to rest as much as I can. You see, I am awakened so early every morning.

JUDGE: Yes, I see your trouble. Well, I advise you, Peter, to take the rooster and the hens into the house.

PETER: (*Surprised*) The rooster and the hens! But, Judge —— !

JUDGE: And if the house still seems crowded to you after that, then take in the geese, too. Good morning to you, Peter. Go and do as I say.

MUSIC: (*Bridge*)

NARRATOR: When Peter had taken the rooster and the hens into his house, the room seemed more crowded than ever. He thought he had better follow the Judge's advice at once, and take the geese in, too. (*Fade*) So he began to shoo the geese into the house.

PETER: Shoo! S-s-s-t! In with you, you silly geese! S-s-s-t!

ANNA: What are you trying to do, Peter?

PETER: I'm trying to get the geese inside.

ANNA: What? The geese must come in, too?

PETER: Yes. The wise Judge said so.

ANNA: Well, if the wise Judge said so, he must have a good reason. All *I* can say is, if these geese can find a place for themselves among the cow, the goat, rooster, the hens, and the feet of the people in this house, then they are not silly geese, but very wise birds. Shoo! Get your beard out of my mixing bowl, you goat!

SOUND: (*Bleat of goat*)

ANNA: And, Peter, chase that hen off the baby's little bed. That's no place to lay eggs. I made a place for that hen in the corner.

SOUND: (*Squawk of hen*)

ANNA: Maria, my daughter, you'd better milk the cow now. I'll peel the potatoes, and then maybe your father can find the time to call Paul from the fields, and we'll all have supper.

MUSIC: (*Bridge*)

NARRATOR: Well, you can imagine what a place that one-room house was by the time the geese joined the rooster, the hens, the goat, and the cow inside the house. There was no space to take two steps in the same direction. And the noise! The geese hissed.

SOUND: (*Hissing of geese*)

NARRATOR: The hens clucked.

SOUND: (*Hens clucking*)

NARRATOR: The rooster crowed.

SOUND: (*Rooster crowing*)

NARRATOR: The goat bleated.

SOUND: (*Bleating of goat*)

NARRATOR: The cow mooed.

SOUND: (*Moo*)

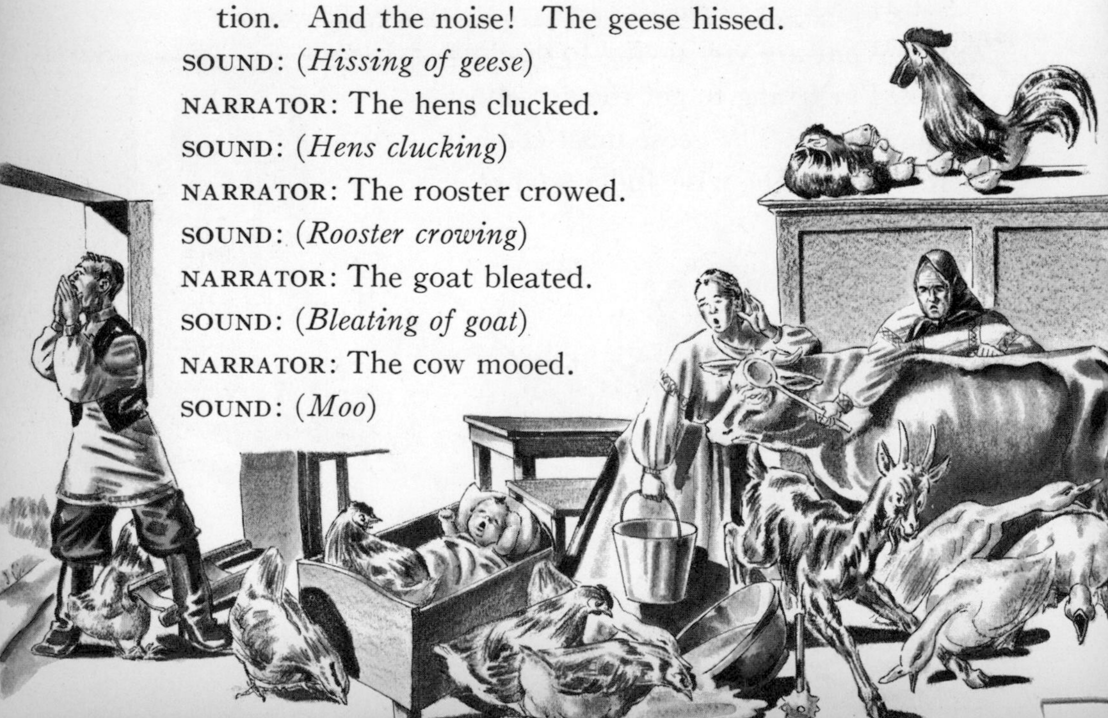

NARRATOR: Peter had little peace and quiet. His wife and daughter were so busy with the housework and the animals, and the son-in-law was so busy in the fields, that they had no time to notice whether the room was crowded or not. As for the baby, he pulled the cow's tail and the goat's beard, and he laughed at the sounds of the rooster and the hens and the geese. (*Fade*) After a few days of this, Peter went to the Judge again.

PETER: Good morning, Judge.

JUDGE: May you have peace, Peter. What's the trouble?

PETER: Peace! I have no peace. My house is so crowded.

JUDGE: What, still too crowded for your comfort?

PETER: Well, to tell the truth, Judge, I have become used to having the animals crowd me from corner to corner. It's the baby, my little grandson, who is really crowded now.

JUDGE: Ah! It's the little one you're thinking of now!

PETER: Yes. The poor little thing has no room to crawl around with all those animals in the way.

JUDGE: Well, in that case, put the rooster and the hens out into the barnyard again.

PETER: Good advice, Judge! That will leave more room for the baby. I'll go and let the chickens out at once.

NARRATOR: Well, with the rooster and the hens out of the house, it was a little roomier, and much quieter. (*Fade*) But soon Peter was back at the Judge's house.

JUDGE: Well, Peter, what brings you back today?

PETER: It's my house, as usual, Judge. I put the rooster and the hens out, as you told me to do.

JUDGE: And don't you find the house less crowded now?

PETER: Oh, yes, indeed! But the geese, Judge!

JUDGE: What about the geese?

PETER: I feel so sorry for the geese. They really should not be kept in a house. They should be outdoors, nibbling at the grass. What shall I do?

JUDGE: I'm glad to see it's the geese, not yourself, you're worried about. In that case, let the geese out.

PETER: Good advice, Judge! Thank you!

MUSIC: (*Bridge*)

NARRATOR: Before long, Peter was back at the Judge's house. (*Fade*) After greeting the Judge, Peter said,

PETER: I have taken your advice, Judge, and my house seems to be growing larger and larger. I have put the geese outdoors again. But the goat, Judge!

JUDGE: What about the goat, Peter?

PETER: The smell of the goat is very strong, you know.

JUDGE: Does it bother you too much?

PETER: I can stand it. But the smell is too strong for the others — my wife, my daughter, and the baby.

JUDGE: Ah! It's because the others can't stand the smell of the goat! In that case, I advise you to put the goat out into the yard again.

PETER: How wise you are, Judge! I'll go at once and let the goat out. But ——

JUDGE: But what, Peter?

PETER: It's about the cow, Judge. It's so big, and it's always getting into the way of my wife and daughter. They work so hard, cooking and cleaning, that it's a pity they should be troubled by the animal.

JUDGE: And doesn't the cow in the house annoy your son-in-law, too?

PETER: I was coming to him. Paul does all my work in the fields for me now. He should have his rest at night without the cow's mooing to disturb him.

JUDGE: I'm glad that at last it is the comfort of your wife and your daughter's family that worries you. You have stopped thinking only of yourself. My advice to you, Peter, is to put the cow back in the field, too.

PETER: Wonderful, Judge! Long life to you for that welcome advice! I'll run and tell the others, and we'll put the goat and the cow out at once.

MUSIC: (*Bridge*)

NARRATOR: Pretty soon Peter was back.

PETER: I had to come back at once, Judge, to tell you how wise and wonderful you are. Your advice has been excellent, every time. The wise King Solomon couldn't have spoken more wisely.

JUDGE: And do you find your house less crowded now, Peter? Is it big enough for all of you now?

PETER: Big? It seems so big now, I feel like a prince, living in a palace.

JUDGE: Did you notice, Peter, that as soon as you began to think of somebody else beside yourself, the house began to grow larger?

PETER: Why, that's so, Judge! I can see that now. And what's more, I must admit now that I am much happier since my daughter and her husband and the baby came to live with us. Ah! That baby! He's a wonder! I must tell you some stories about him. But first, let me give you this fine fat goose as thanks for your advice.

MUSIC: (*Up full and out*)

ANNOUNCER: And that is how the Judge taught Peter that the best way to be happy and comfortable was to think about others instead of worrying about himself.

Our next story will be *The Golden Touch*, a story from Greece.

The Golden

CAST King Midas · Bacchus · Demetrius · Marigold · Announcer · Narrator

SOUNDS

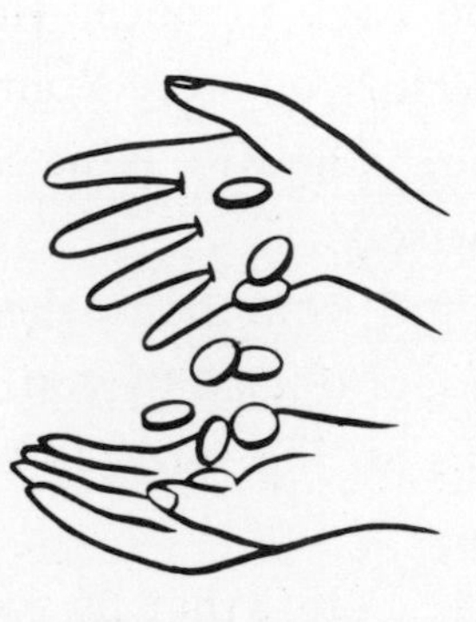

Clink of coins

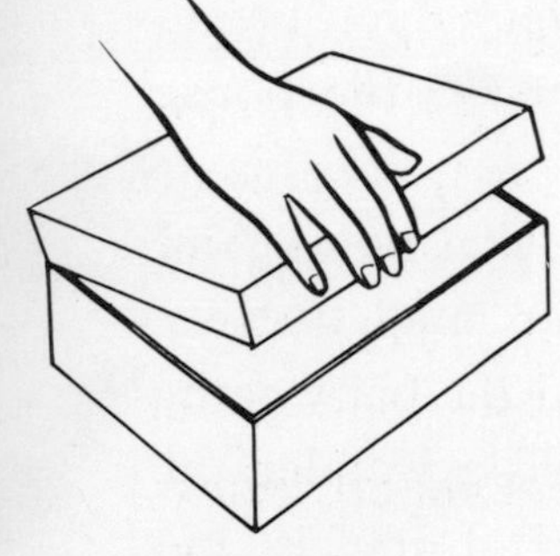

Door open

Click of spoon

ANNOUNCER: Hello, boys and girls. It's story time again. Today we will tell you a story about a wish that came true and the trouble that it caused. Listen to the story of *The Golden Touch.*

MUSIC: (*Up and out*)

Touch

NARRATOR: Once upon a time, when the world was young, there lived in Greece a king named Midas. There were two things that King Midas loved above all else. One was gold, and the other was his little daughter. King Midas collected gold and precious things made of gold, and he had boxes full of treasure stored in a large room deep under his palace. There he often went to count his pieces of gold. But Midas loved his little daughter Marigold even more than he loved his golden treasure.

One day King Midas went down to the treasure room under his palace to count his gold pieces. He unlocked his strong boxes and ran his fingers through the heaps of coins, (*Fade*) talking to them as if they were alive.

SOUND: (*Clink of coins under*)

MIDAS: Ah! My gold! My beautiful, shining pieces of gold! You are the most beautiful sight in the world. I have taken you wherever I found you. I have won you in battle, and my ships have brought you back in trade from far lands. The sound you make as I toss you from hand to hand is sweeter to my ears than any music I've ever heard. What a lucky man I am to have all this gold!

SOUND: (*Coins out*)

BACCHUS: (*Light laugh*) Are you sure of that, King Midas?

MIDAS: (*Startled*) Who said that?

BACCHUS: Look behind you, Midas.

MIDAS: Oh! How did you get in? I locked the door of this room myself.

BACCHUS: Your eyes are still filled with the light of your gold, or you would know who I am and how I entered.

MIDAS: There is a sort of golden light around you, too. No ordinary man could have entered this room without my knowing it. Can it be that you are one of the mighty gods, come down to visit the earth?

BACCHUS: Yes. I am Bacchus, god of the vine and grapes.

MIDAS: Oh! Now I see the grape leaves around your head.

BACCHUS: It is not often that we gods allow ordinary men to see us on our visits to the earth, Midas.

MIDAS: I feel honored by this visit, Bacchus. May I know why I am honored like this?

BACCHUS: It is because you helped one of the other gods when he was visiting among men a short time ago. I am grateful to you for that, Midas, and I have come to do you a favor in return.

MIDAS: That is very good of you, Bacchus. What will this favor be?

BACCHUS: I shall grant you one wish. You may have the one thing your heart desires most.

MIDAS: One thing! I must decide carefully. And yet, there is only one thing that could make me happy.

BACCHUS: Name it, Midas, and you shall have it.

MIDAS: It is so much trouble to collect my golden treasures from here, there, and everywhere. I wish — you are sure I may have any wish I make?

BACCHUS: Yes, anything. Go on, Midas. You wish ——?

MIDAS: I wish that everything I touch shall at once be turned to gold.

BACCHUS: The golden touch! Are you sure you want it?

MIDAS: I am sure, Bacchus.

BACCHUS: You are a very rich man now, Midas. This room holds more gold than any one man ever had.

MIDAS: I have done pretty well, but not well enough to suit me. After all, it has taken me all my life to collect this little store of gold.

BACCHUS: The golden touch! Are you sure it will satisfy you?

MIDAS: Nothing else will make me so happy.

BACCHUS: And are you sure you will never be sorry that your touch will change everything to gold?

MIDAS: How could I ever regret such a thing?

BACCHUS: Very well, Midas. Tomorrow morning at sunrise you will find that you have the golden touch. (*Fade*) May you enjoy your power! Farewell, Midas.

NARRATOR: The god Bacchus disappeared as silently and quickly as he had come. King Midas looked at the gold around him, thinking how much more he would have the next day, and then went up to his rooms in the palace. He was a long time falling asleep that night. His mind was filled with thoughts of the happiness in store for him when he should have the golden touch. At last he fell asleep.

MUSIC: (*Up and under*)

NARRATOR: The first sunbeams stealing into the window wakened King Midas the next morning. There was something yellow and shining on his bed. For a moment he wondered what it was. Then he remembered the golden touch. The sheets and blanket on his bed were now made of golden threads. The pillowcase under his head felt strangely stiff too. He turned and saw that it, too, was of spun gold. The first gleam of the sun had brought him the golden touch!

MUSIC: (*Up full and out quickly*)

NARRATOR: (*Fade*) King Midas sprang out of bed, crying out,

MIDAS: The golden touch! The god Bacchus has kept his promise! I must touch everything around me to see if it's really true! The posts of my bed. Gold! My slippers! They are changed to cloth of gold as my feet slip into them! I must put on my clothes quickly and see what else I can change to gold to add to my treasures. Ah! My clothes, too, are changing. What a magnificent robe of cloth of gold! No other king was ever dressed so handsomely. I must call my servant.

SOUND: (*Claps hands*)

MIDAS: Ho there, Demetrius!

SOUND: (*Door opens*)

DEMETRIUS: (*Fade in*) Good morning, King Midas.

MIDAS: It's a glorious morning, Demetrius!

DEMETRIUS: Your Majesty is awake early. Oh!

MIDAS: Why do you stare so, Demetrius?

DEMETRIUS: The bed, your Majesty. I've never seen that bed before.

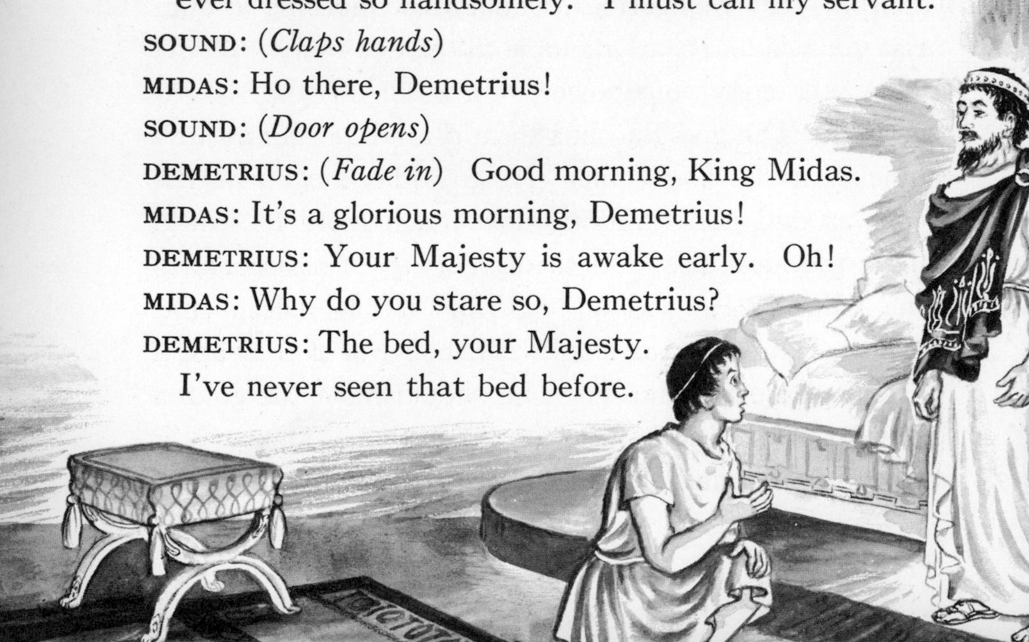

MIDAS: Oh, yes, you have. It's been here for years.

DEMETRIUS: But the posts are made of gold. And the bedclothes, the sheets and the blanket — cloth of gold! And the robe you are wearing, your Majesty! I know that was never in your wardrobe before.

MIDAS: You are partly right, Demetrius. It's not a new robe, and yet it is. I changed the cloth to gold.

DEMETRIUS: You changed ——?

MIDAS: The robe is a little heavy, I admit, but it is gold.

DEMETRIUS: How could you change it? Your Majesty is joking.

MIDAS: I'm not joking. I have the golden touch!

DEMETRIUS: I would think you had dreamed that, if I didn't see all these things changed to gold. How did it happen, if it pleases you to tell me?

MIDAS: The story is too long. All I can tell you now is that Bacchus, god of the vine, granted me this power, beginning at sunrise this morning.

DEMETRIUS: Truly a wonderful gift, King Midas! But do not touch my clothes, your Majesty. It is not fitting that your servant's clothing should be of gold, like yours.

MIDAS: No, I won't do that. Go and order my breakfast now, Demetrius.

DEMETRIUS: Certainly, your Majesty. What would you like for breakfast this morning?

MIDAS: I'm too excited to be very hungry this morning. All I want is a boiled egg, bread and butter, a little honey, and some milk.

DEMETRIUS: Very well, your Majesty.

MIDAS: While breakfast is being prepared, I shall walk in the garden and see how my roses are getting on.

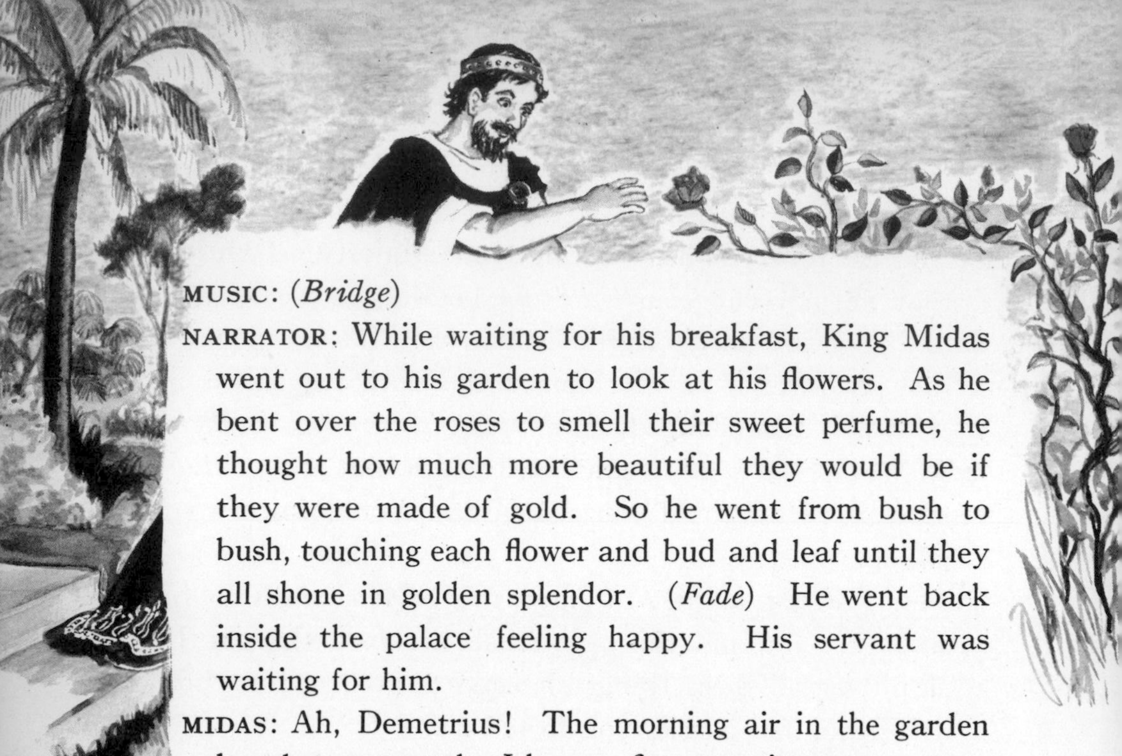

MUSIC: (*Bridge*)

NARRATOR: While waiting for his breakfast, King Midas went out to his garden to look at his flowers. As he bent over the roses to smell their sweet perfume, he thought how much more beautiful they would be if they were made of gold. So he went from bush to bush, touching each flower and bud and leaf until they all shone in golden splendor. (*Fade*) He went back inside the palace feeling happy. His servant was waiting for him.

MIDAS: Ah, Demetrius! The morning air in the garden has done me good. I have a fine appetite now.

DEMETRIUS: I'm very glad, your Majesty. Shall I open the egg for you?

MIDAS: Yes, do.

SOUND: (*Click of spoon*)

MIDAS: Tell the cook that the egg was boiled just right, not too soft and not too hard.

DEMETRIUS: Shall I sprinkle the salt on it for you, King Midas?

MIDAS: No, thank you, Demetrius. I'll do that myself. Oh! The salt shaker has turned to gold in my hand! Lucky for me that I do not have to touch the salt inside. Eating gold dust on my egg would be very funny.

DEMETRIUS: Perhaps, your Majesty.

MIDAS: Look! The silver spoon changes to gold in my hand! Well, a king may have golden tableware, though I like simple things to eat with. (*Choking cough*) Oh!

DEMETRIUS: What's wrong, your Majesty?

MIDAS: The egg turns into a lump of gold when it touches my mouth! I can't eat it!

DEMETRIUS: That's too bad, your Majesty. Try the bread. I'll butter it for you, so you won't have to touch it. There! I'll hold it for you while you bite into it.

MIDAS: Mmm! The bread, too, turns to hard gold when I try to take a bite of it. What shall I do? I'm hungry, and I can't eat.

DEMETRIUS: Try the milk, King Midas. Drink it down quickly.

MIDAS: I'll try it. (*Choking cough*) The milk, too, changes to gold the moment it touches my lips. I can't eat or drink. What shall I do?

DEMETRIUS: I don't know, I'm sure, your Majesty. I never heard of a king who could not eat or drink.

MIDAS: Must I, the King, starve to death in the midst of all my gold? The lowest servant in my palace can sit down and satisfy his hunger. The poorest man in my kingdom can eat, though he may have only a crust of bread and a cup of milk for his meal.

DEMETRIUS: It may be, your Majesty, that the golden touch is not such a wonderful gift to have, after all.

MIDAS: Oh, well, this is the first meal I've tried to eat since I've had the golden touch. There must be a way to eat and keep the golden touch, too.

In the meantime, Demetrius, take these lumps of gold that were parts of my breakfast and put them on a plate. I'll lock them up in my treasure room. They're still gold.

DEMETRIUS: Very well, your Majesty.

MARIGOLD: (*Fade in, sobbing*) Father! Oh, Father! Where are you?

MIDAS: Here, Marigold darling, at the table. Come and say good morning to me.

MARIGOLD: Oh, Father! The most awful thing has happened!

MIDAS: I don't like to see my little daughter crying. What awful thing has happened? Has your kitten run away?

MARIGOLD: No, Father. It's the roses in the garden. The beautiful red and white roses are all gone!

MIDAS: All gone? How can that be? Why, I saw them all in the garden just a little while ago.

MARIGOLD: But they are not flowers any more. They are all hard and stiff and shiny yellow now, and they used to be red and white and soft as velvet.

MIDAS: They have changed to gold, dear. Don't you think the roses are much prettier this way?

MARIGOLD: No, I don't. They used to smell so sweet, and now they're just hard and don't smell at all. Oh, they're hateful! I want my lovely roses back! (*Weeps*)

MIDAS: You'll grow to love them this way, as golden flowers. You haven't kissed me good morning yet.

MARIGOLD: Oh, I'm sorry, Father! I was so upset at the sight of those ugly flowers. Good morning, Fa——

MIDAS: Marigold! What's the matter? Your face is so cold. What's wrong? Oh! How terrible! My touch has changed you into a statue of gold! Your warm little body is cold and stiff! Your rosy face and your soft brown curls are hard and yellow. You are not my little girl any more, but a golden statue. Oh! What have I done to you? If I could only make you live again! I'd give all my gold to have you back.

BACCHUS: (*Softly*) Well, King Midas?

MIDAS: Oh! It's you again, Bacchus.

BACCHUS: Yes. I have come down to the earth again, to see how you like the golden touch. Are you happy now, Midas, as happy as you thought you'd be?

MIDAS: Happy? I've never been so miserable!

BACCHUS: You were sure that the golden touch was the one thing you wanted to make you happy.

MIDAS: I was a fool. I can't eat, I can't drink, I'm in danger of starving to death. Worst of all, I've changed the one person I love best in the world into a hard lump of yellow metal. I wish I had never seen gold!

BACCHUS: So you think now that gold is not the best way to happiness?

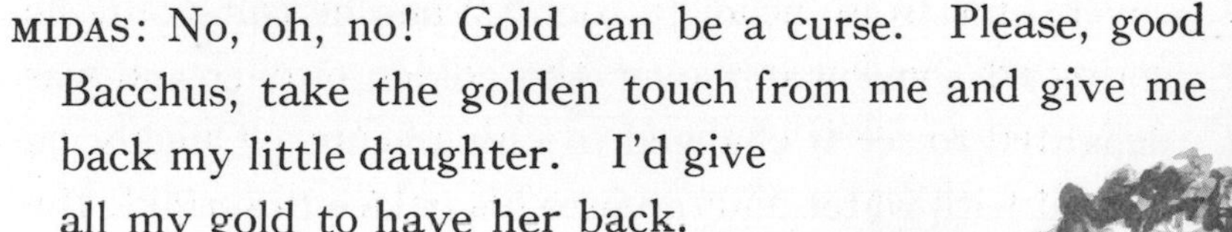

MIDAS: No, oh, no! Gold can be a curse. Please, good Bacchus, take the golden touch from me and give me back my little daughter. I'd give all my gold to have her back.

BACCHUS: Very well, Midas. As soon as the sun sets, go and bathe in the river that runs through your garden. Let the water come over your head. When you come out you will have lost the golden touch.

MIDAS: That will be fine, Bacchus, to be rid of that awful power. But what about my daughter? Isn't there some way you can bring her back to life? I could not bear to keep looking at a statue which should be a laughing little girl, knowing that I took life from her.

BACCHUS: If you will sprinkle some of the river water over her, she will become as she was before. You can do this with anything else you wish to change back to what it was.

MIDAS: Oh, thank you, Bacchus! Oh, to have my little daughter back again! Never again shall I believe that gold is the most important thing in the world.

MUSIC: (*Bridge*)

NARRATOR: Late in the afternoon King Midas stood by the river that flowed through his garden. At his feet stood a golden pitcher which he had ready to fill with water to sprinkle over his little daughter. Just as the sun set, Midas slipped into the river, letting the water cover him from head to toe. When he came out, he sprinkled some water over the golden pitcher and was delighted to see it changed to china again. Quickly he filled it with water and ran into his palace to sprinkle the water over little Marigold. You can imagine his happiness when he saw her body grow soft and the rosy color come back to her face. She sighed and blinked her eyes as she came alive again. (*Fade*) King Midas held out his arms to her.

MIDAS: Marigold, my darling!

MARIGOLD: Good evening, Father. Why do you look so strangely at me? Oh! I am wet from head to foot. What happened? Did I fall into the river?

MIDAS: No, my dear. I splashed the water from this pitcher over you.

MARIGOLD: Oh, don't worry about it, Father. I'll run to my room and change my dress.

MIDAS: I'll wait here for you, dear. But when you return, you must come out into the garden with me and help me water our favorite roses.

MARIGOLD: But why? That is the gardener's work.

MIDAS: Oh, I have some special water I want to try on them. Run along now and change your dress. I'll tell you about it while we're sprinkling the roses.

NARRATOR: King Midas told Marigold a little about the golden touch as they changed the golden roses back to soft, fragrant, red and white ones. But he did not tell her that she herself had been changed into a statue.

As long as King Midas lived, there were two things that always reminded him of the golden touch. One was the sand in the river. The sand had turned to gold when he had first stepped into it, and had remained that way. The other thing was a streak of gold in Marigold's hair, which never changed its color. As for King Midas himself, he used to say that he hated the sight of all things golden except the bright, sunny light of his daughter's hair.

MUSIC: (*Up and out*)

ANNOUNCER: So King Midas found that getting the one thing he thought he wanted didn't make him happy after all. Our next tale comes from America. It is called *The Young Paul Bunyan*. We know you will like it.

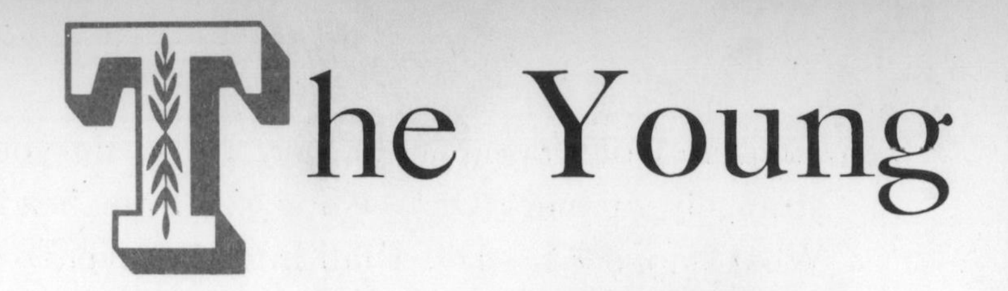

The Young

CAST

FATHER	THIRD NEIGHBOR
MOTHER	FOURTH NEIGHBOR
PAUL	FARMER
WOMAN	SHIPBUILDER
FIRST NEIGHBOR	GOVERNOR-GENERAL
SECOND NEIGHBOR	ANNOUNCER

NARRATOR

SOUNDS

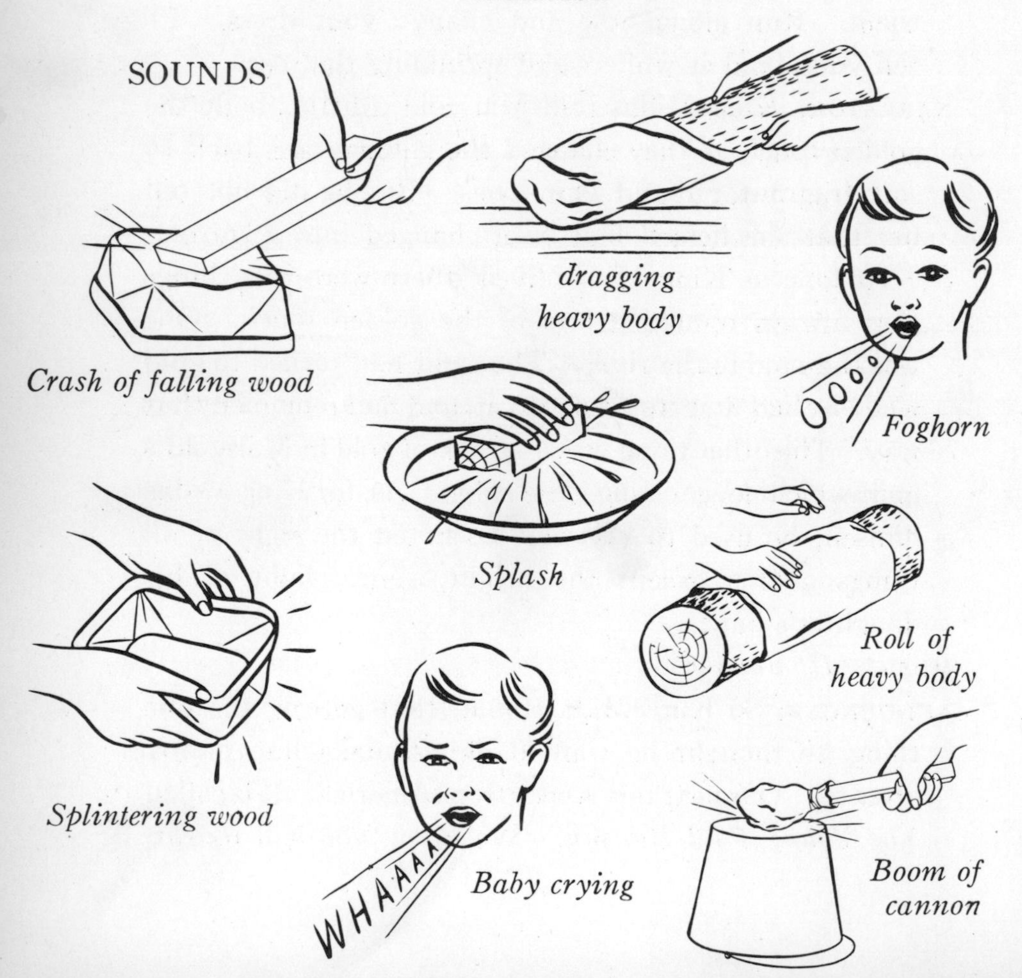

Crash of falling wood

dragging heavy body

Foghorn

Splash

Splintering wood

Roll of heavy body

Baby crying

Boom of cannon

Paul Bunyan

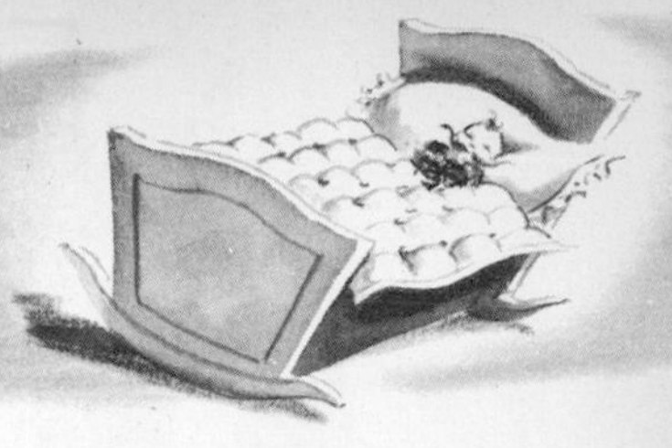

ANNOUNCER: Today you will hear a story about one of the heroes of pioneer days in North America. In those days there was much hard work to be done. Trees had to be cut down, land had to be cleared, cattle had to be herded, and many other hard jobs had to be done. The pioneers really admired a man who could do a better day's work than his neighbors, so most of the stories they told were about men who could do some kind of work better than anyone else.

These stories were told over and over; they were changed and added to, until now no one really knows whether any of the story was true to begin with. The stories about these mighty workers are now American folk tales.

One of the great heroes of these American folk tales is Paul Bunyan, the giant of the lumber camps. Some people say that Paul Bunyan's name was really Paul Bonjean, that he was born in Canada, and that his parents were French.

This is the story they tell of Paul's childhood and of how he came to be Paul Bunyan, the greatest of the lumberjacks.

MUSIC: (*Bridge*)

NARRATOR: From the minute he was born it was plain to be seen that Paul Bonjean was going to be a hero. His father was very proud of the baby. When Papa Bonjean heard the baby's first cry, (*Fade*) he said to the neighbor woman who had come in to help,

FATHER: Ah! What a baby! Did you ever hear a newborn baby cry like that? Listen!

SOUND: (*Loud crying of baby up and out*)

WOMAN: In truth, never have I heard such a voice from a baby just a few minutes old.

FATHER: Is it any wonder, Madame? Most babies, they weigh seven, eight, maybe nine pounds. But my son — I shall name him Paul — my Paul, he weighs seventy pounds!

WOMAN: And never did I see a baby born with such a face. Already he has a black beard and curly moustaches!

FATHER: That is a sign that he will be a strong man. He will help me with my fishing. I can hardly wait till he is a grown young man. What a baby!

MUSIC: (*Bridge*)

NARRATOR: Well, Paul's father didn't have to wait long till his son was grown-up in size, if not in years. Paul kept growing that very first day he was born. Proud though his parents had been in the morning, (*Fade*) by the time night came they were very much worried.

FATHER: Our young Paul, he has drunk up all the milk that our cow has given today. Never have I seen a young baby drink milk like that!

MOTHER: And what shall we do for clothing for him? The little baby clothes I made for him, they do not fit on one of his arms at the end of his first day.

FATHER: And where shall we put him to sleep? The cabin bed is too small for him. It is not right that a baby one day old should sleep on the floor.

MOTHER: And the diapers I got ready for him, they are like pocket handkerchiefs for him. I must use sheets, and where am I to get so many bed sheets?

FATHER: We must ask the neighbors to help. (*Proud*) Ah, but our Paul, he is a very fine baby! Never was there such a baby in all Canada, in all the world!

MUSIC: (*Bridge*)

NARRATOR: The neighbors came to the aid of Paul's parents as well as they could. They all sent milk from their cows for Paul to drink. They lent their sheets for diapers and their blankets for his bed. And where do you suppose they made up a bed for the newborn baby? In the ox shed. They padded the floor and the walls of the ox stall with soft blankets.

The next morning the whole village was gathered outside the Bonjean ox shed, waiting to see the wonderful baby. Paul, it was plain, had kept on growing during the night.

FIRST NEIGHBOR: How big the little one has become! See, his hands and feet are sticking out through the doors and windows of the shed.

SOUND: (*Loud crying of baby. Sound of splintering wood*)

SECOND NEIGHBOR: Ah! He has stretched out an arm, and he has knocked out the wall of the shed!

THIRD NEIGHBOR: He is strong as an ox himself, that little one. Stand back, everyone! He is kicking his legs! Watch out for that tree!

SOUND: (*Crash of falling wood*)

THIRD NEIGHBOR: The baby Paul
has kicked out his legs and knocked down a tree!

FOURTH NEIGHBOR: Papa Bonjean! What will you do with your baby? He is too big for your little place.

FATHER: Ah! It is a great worry, truly. Something will have to be done. My good wife and I, we must put our heads together and think.

MUSIC: (*Bridge*)

NARRATOR: So Paul's parents put their heads together and thought. They decided that they could do very little for their unusual baby without calling on their neighbors for help. The greatest problem was food. Most of the neighbors were glad to help. (*Fade*) They said,

FIRST NEIGHBOR: Do not worry about milk for the little Paul. We will gather together all the cows in this province of Canada, and all the milk that they give shall be for Paul to drink.

NARRATOR: And then, of course, the baby had to have his cod-liver oil to keep him strong and healthy. How much cod-liver oil does an ordinary baby take each day? About a teaspoonful, doesn't he? Well, young Paul Bonjean had to have three barrelfuls every day! (*Fade*) Papa Bonjean rubbed his head and said,

FATHER: All that cod-liver oil! How can I buy it? I am not a rich man, only a fisherman.

NARRATOR: And the neighbors answered,

SECOND NEIGHBOR: Do not worry about cod-liver oil for the little Paul. We will all lend you money to buy it. You can pay it back when Paul is older and starts working.

FATHER: But where can I find so much cod-liver oil? Three barrels a day! That makes many barrels a month.

THIRD NEIGHBOR: Do not worry about that, Papa Bonjean. In the harbor are several ships loaded with barrels of cod-liver oil. We will buy all the barrels of oil and store them for you in the village warehouse.

FATHER: Ah! That is wonderful of you! Never did a man have such good neighbors!

MUSIC: (*Bridge*)

NARRATOR: So that helped solve the problem of food for the little Paul's earliest days. Then there was the matter of clothes. A sailmaker kindly gave the parents several large sails, the size that were used on the largest sailing vessels. These sails were made up into shirts and short trousers for baby Paul. You'll never guess what the buttons on his clothes were. Wagon wheels! Almost as important as the little Paul's food was a place for him to sleep. No house was big enough, no barn strong enough. (*Fade*) Papa Bonjean went to a farmer and asked,

FATHER: Please, good farmer, will you allow me to spread the baby's blankets in your wheat field?

FARMER: But how can you ask that, Papa Bonjean? The blankets would cover my whole field, and if Paul sleeps in it, what will become of my wheat? It will all be crushed, and I shall have none to sell.

FATHER: What, then? The little baby must have his sleep to grow and to keep healthy.

FARMER: You must think up some other place. My wheat field you may not have. No, no!

MUSIC: (*Bridge*)

NARRATOR: Well, the neighbors put their heads together and thought. By and by somebody had a bright idea. A few of them went down to a shipyard in Maine. There they found a ship that was only partly built and had no decks or masts on it yet. It looked like a perfect cradle for a baby giant or a giant baby like Paul. The neighbors bought the unfinished ship. When they asked to have the hull lined with soft mattresses, the shipbuilder opened his eyes wide.

SHIPBUILDER: What's that? Line the hull with mattresses?

FIRST NEIGHBOR: Yes, that's right. This ship, you see, is going to be a cradle for a baby.

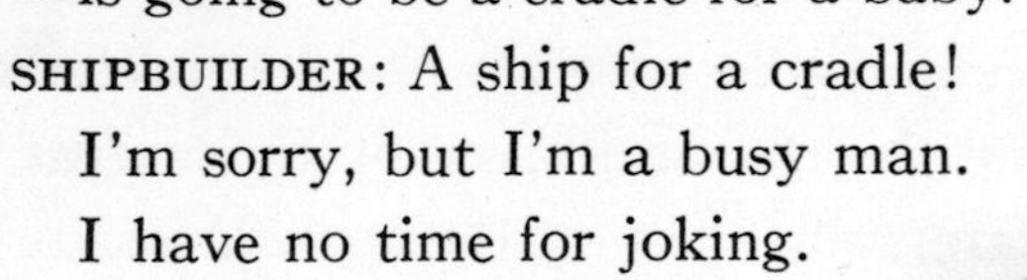

SHIPBUILDER: A ship for a cradle!
I'm sorry, but I'm a busy man.
I have no time for joking.

SECOND NEIGHBOR: We are not trying to joke with you. Our little Paul Bonjean, he is no ordinary baby. He is only a few days old, and already he is as tall as a hill.

SHIPBUILDER: That is a miracle!

THIRD NEIGHBOR: You speak truly, sir. The little Paul is a nine days' wonder, and our village is very proud of him. You must have this ship hull lined with mattresses by tomorrow morning, so we can tow it up to the Bay of Fundy, to the shores of our village.

SHIPBUILDER: But how will you get this wonder baby into the ship cradle, if he is as big as you say?

FIRST NEIGHBOR: Oh, that will be easy. We will pick him up with a derrick and lower him gently into the cradle.

SHIPBUILDER: Picking up a baby with a derrick! That is a sight I have yet to see!

MUSIC: (*Bridge*)

NARRATOR: That is exactly how the little Paul was placed in his cradle. The ship hull made a fine bed for him, not too big, not too small. He fell fast asleep at once. The waves rocked him gently, as a mother would have rocked her baby's cradle. Yes, Paul slept soundly. For two whole weeks at a stretch he slept! That was a terrible time for little Paul's parents. He had to have his bottle, but he could not be waked. They appealed to the neighbors, and pretty soon everybody in that part of Canada was trying to wake baby Paul Bonjean. First, Papa Bonjean rowed out to the ship and called,

FATHER: Paul! Paul, my little one! Wake up! It's time for your milk and cod-liver oil. Wake up, my little one!

NARRATOR: But little Paul slept on. Then a group of fishermen rowed out to the cradle and shouted together,

VOICES: Paul! Wake up, little Paul! Wake up, little Paul!

NARRATOR: But Paul slept on. Papa Bonjean went to the keeper of the lighthouse and begged him to sound the foghorn. The lighthouse keeper sounded the foghorn.

SOUND: (*Deep horn blowing*)

NARRATOR: But little Paul slept on. Then Papa Bonjean went to the Mayor for help. But the Mayor could think of nothing. He went to the Governor of the Province of New Brunswick. The Governor of the Province had no idea what to do, either, so he went to the Governor-General of Canada. Papa Bonjean and the Mayor went along, too. And the Governor-General had an idea!

GOVERNOR-GENERAL: You want to know how to wake up a baby who is so big he must have a ship for a cradle? But it is a simple matter. The British Navy, you know!

FATHER: The British Navy, your Excellency?

GOVERNOR-GENERAL: Yes, Papa Bonjean. Part of the British Navy is stationed off the coast. I will send a message to the Admiral and ask him to wake up the baby. Do not worry any longer. The Admiral will carry out this task with credit to the British Navy.

FATHER: Oh, thank you a thousand times, your Excellency.

MUSIC: (*Bridge*)

NARRATOR: Well, the Governor-General of all Canada sent a message to the Admiral of the British Navy. Now the Admiral was very fond of children, so he agreed to help. He ordered his ships to sail into the Bay of Fundy and lined them up in battle formation near little Paul's cradle. Then the Admiral shouted his orders, and all the guns of all the ships fired high over the cradle.

SOUND: (*Boom of cannon*)

NARRATOR: Well, that did wake little Paul! He let out a cry for his mother, as any frightened baby would.

PAUL: (*Very loud*) Mama! Mama!

NARRATOR: That frightened cry of little Paul was heard from the Bay of Fundy clear down to Boston. Not only did Paul scream, but he shook so that his cradle rocked from side to side, sending the water up in waves seventy-five feet high. Even today the water in the Bay of Fundy hasn't calmed down. The tide comes up as high as fifty feet or more. Some people blame this high tide on the waves that the baby Paul set up when he was frightened by the cannon of the British Navy.

MUSIC: (*Bridge*)

NARRATOR: Well, all this sounds as if the little Paul were in for a bad time in childhood. But as he grew up — and how he grew up! — he had a good time.

He went to school with the other children, though he did have his troubles with things like books and paper. He wrote so large that he could get only one letter on a sheet of paper, and his books were so large they had to be carried back and forth on an oxcart.

It didn't take Paul long to learn everything that little village school could teach him, so he left school. After a few weeks his father said to him,

FATHER: Well, Paul, my son, what will you do now? You must work if you do not go to school.

PAUL: But, Papa, I do not know what work I want to do.

FATHER: You are a good fisherman. Why not do that?

PAUL: Fishing is too easy. In the morning I put a fishing schooner under each arm and I wade out to the deep water of the ocean. Then I scoop the fish out of the water, fill the schooners, and wade back to the shore.

FATHER: You are the best fisherman in the province.

PAUL: Yes, but it is not exciting enough for me.

FATHER: What about hunting, Paul?

PAUL: Hunting is not exciting for me, either, Papa. It is too easy, especially since I invented the shotgun that shoots seventy-six bullets, one right after the other. No, I do not care for hunting or fishing. But don't worry, Papa. I will think up something interesting to do.

NARRATOR: Then Paul packed some books and some food and walked off across the countryside to think over what he wanted to do. By the ocean he found a cave big enough for him and stayed there, reading and thinking, all winter.

One day a terrific noise woke Paul suddenly out of his daydreaming. Something heavy fell off the roof of his cave and splashed into the ocean.

SOUND: (*Roll of heavy body, followed by loud splash*)

NARRATOR: Paul dashed out of his cave. To his great surprise he saw that the ground was covered with deep snow of a strange blue color. Sticking out of the water were the horns and head of a baby ox. Paul waded into the water and started to pull the baby ox to shore. It was heavy work, even for the strong Paul.

SOUND: (*Splashing, grunting, dragging of heavy body*)

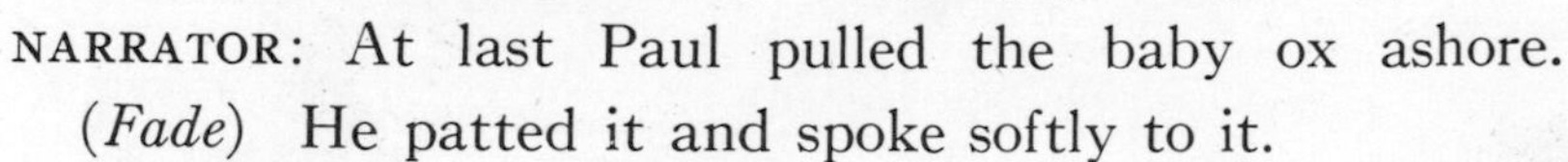

NARRATOR: At last Paul pulled the baby ox ashore. (*Fade*) He patted it and spoke softly to it.

PAUL: Ah! You are a fine young ox. You're beautiful. Never have I seen such a big, strong baby ox. And such hair! Bright blue as this strange blue snow on the ground. I shall call you Bébé, as the French call all babies, and you shall be my friend and companion. At last I have a companion strong enough for me to play with. Holà, Bébé! We will have sport together!

MUSIC: (*Bridge*)

NARRATOR: And Bébé, the blue ox, was a fitting companion for Paul, for it was as big and strong for an ox as Paul was big and strong for a man. (*Fade*) Then one day Paul said to Bébé, the blue ox,

PAUL: Bébé, my friend, I feel I am about to find out what my life work is to be. I feel, too, that this work is not to be done here by the ocean. Holà, Bébé, we shall step across the rivers and forests and see what work we can find to do. Come, Bébé!

NARRATOR: So he packed a lunch, and with Bébé, the blue ox, Paul Bonjean started out. Bébé skipped along ahead, and whenever a tree got in the way, Bébé knocked it over. The trees fell crashing left and right. As Paul watched the trees falling, he suddenly knew what his life work would be.

PAUL: Ah! At last it comes to me! I will cut down the trees in the forests. I must make room for the pioneers who will want to build cities and make farms! The trees will give wood for houses and boats and furniture.

I'll build logging camps all over America! Yes, sirree! I shall invent logging. I'll dig lakes and rivers to float the logs on. I'll be the best lumberjack that ever lived!

NARRATOR: And all the things that Paul said then came true. Before long, Paul had started logging camps in places all over America where there were trees to be cut.

Paul taught other men in those camps how logging should be done, but of course no one else ever could do it as well as he did. In the camps, Paul worked with men from many different countries. Not many of them could speak French, and they found that Bonjean was a hard name for them to say. After a while everyone called him Paul Bunyan, and the big blue ox was called Babe.

Paul did so many marvelous things that in logging camps all over America, men still tell of the wonderful deeds of Paul Bunyan, king of the lumberjacks.

MUSIC: (*Up and out*)

ANNOUNCER: This is just the beginning of the story of Paul Bunyan. Perhaps you can find a book in which there are other stories about Paul Bunyan and can read more about the greatest lumberjack that ever lived.

Be sure to listen for our next story, which comes from the Near East. It is called *The Christmas Angel*.

The Christmas

CAST		
	Theodosia	First Girl
	Martha	First Boy
	Christmas Angel	Second Girl
	Paul	Second Boy
	Mother	Announcer
	Miss Mary	Narrator

SOUNDS

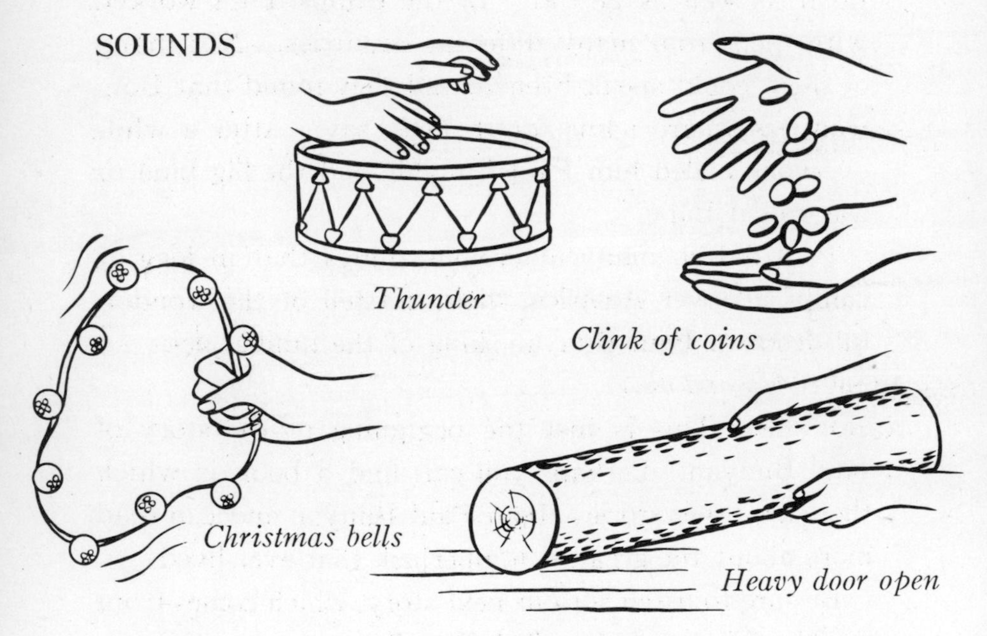

ANNOUNCER: Hello, boys and girls. It's time for another one of our *Tales from the Four Winds*. Today we have a Christmas story which comes from a country in the Near East. Listen to our story of *The Christmas Angel.*

MUSIC: (*Christmas music up and out*)

Angel

NARRATOR: Once upon a time there lived in a country in the Near East a princess named Theodosia. One Christmas morning, the church bells woke the little Princess very early. (*Fade*) She went over to her maid's bed and said,

THEODOSIA: Martha! Martha! Wake up, Martha!

MARTHA: (*Sleepy*) Good morning, Princess Theodosia. Why are you out of bed at this hour?

THEODOSIA: It's Christmas morning. Can't you hear the church bells?

MARTHA: Yes, I hear them. But it is very early. You had better go back to bed.

THEODOSIA: I won't go back to bed! I want to go down to the Great Hall and see my Christmas presents.

MARTHA: But nobody else is stirring, Princess. Why not wait until the hour when everybody will be going to look at their gifts?

THEODOSIA: Why should I wait if I don't want to? I want my gifts now. You're my maid, Martha. I command you to come with me!

MARTHA: Very well, Princess. Wait till I put on my robe.

MUSIC: (*Bridge*)

THEODOSIA: I can hardly wait to see my Christmas presents, Martha. There must be a great many of them. Open the door of the Great Hall. Quick!

SOUND: (*Heavy door open*)

MARTHA: The names of the King and Queen and all the other members of the royal palace are written on tablets on the walls, you know, Princess. The gifts are placed under their names. Let's see. Where is yours?

THEODOSIA: I know just where it is, Martha. I looked for it yesterday, before the gifts were put down. I'm twelve, the youngest in the palace, so my place is at the other end of the Hall.

MARTHA: Oh, what beautiful gifts in the Queen's pile! Look, Princess.

THEODOSIA: I don't care what anybody else is getting. (*Fade*) All I care about is my own gifts.

MARTHA: Don't run, Princess. You'll slip on the marble floor.

THEODOSIA: (*Off mike*) Oh! Oh! How dare they treat me like this!

MARTHA: What's the matter? Why, there's nothing under your name, Princess, except a small black bag.

THEODOSIA: And look what it says on the card tied on the handle, Martha.

MARTHA: "This is for the selfish Princess Theodosia."

THEODOSIA: What a mean trick to play on me! But wait a minute. There may be something pretty inside it — perhaps the string of pearls I've been wanting so much.

MARTHA: (*Doubtful*) Perhaps.

THEODOSIA: But the bag is locked, and I don't see any key.

SOUND: (*Thunder*)

THEODOSIA: Oh! This blinding light! Martha! Martha! I'm frightened! Where are you, Martha?

ANGEL: (*Quiet voice*) Martha isn't here, Theodosia. I have sent her away.

THEODOSIA: Who is talking? This light is so bright, I can't see.

ANGEL: I am the Christmas Angel.

THEODOSIA: (*Awed*) Now I can see your face and your wings. You are an angel, yet I am not frightened now.

ANGEL: Why should you be afraid of me, child?

THEODOSIA: I have not always been a good girl. Have you come to remind me of the times I was bad?

ANGEL: No. Those times are past. I have come to help you.

THEODOSIA: Oh! Then please open this black bag that was left as a Christmas gift for me. It may hold some lovely things — a string of pearls, I hope.

ANGEL: The bag is locked tight, isn't it? What a pity!

THEODOSIA: I hope there are treasures in it. But I have no key.

ANGEL: Poor child! You don't know the secret that unlocks all treasures, do you?

THEODOSIA: Can you help me learn this secret?

ANGEL: I hope so. Come with me, Theodosia, and we shall see if you can learn.

THEODOSIA: Where will you take me?

ANGEL: Hold my hand, and we will fly together over the city. Keep the black bag in your other hand.

THEODOSIA: But won't people stare at me, flying in the sky?

ANGEL: They will not see you. The shadow of my wings will make you as invisible as I am. Only on special occasions does an angel allow men to see him, you know. Give me your hand now, child.

MUSIC: (*Christmas music up and out*)

THEODOSIA: How quiet the streets are, Christmas Angel!

ANGEL: It is Christmas morning. All sounds of work are stilled. Tell me, Theodosia. Do you know the meaning of Christmas?

THEODOSIA: It means, "Peace on earth, good will to men."

ANGEL: You say those words easily enough, but I wonder if you really know what they mean. We'll stop here outside the window of this little cottage.

THEODOSIA: What a miserable place to live! Just one room with a fireplace in one corner. It must be very cold in there; so many windowpanes are broken.

ANGEL: Would you like to be that little boy, shivering in the bed? (*Fade*) Listen to him.

PAUL: I'm cold, Mother! This blanket is so thin.

MOTHER: (*Cheerfully*) I know, Paul. But wrap it around you more tightly while I light the fire in the fireplace. There will be a beautiful blaze soon!

PAUL: But those few sticks won't last very long, Mother.

MOTHER: Oh, it's Christmas morning, dear, so let's pretend we have a roaring fire that will burn bright and keep us warm all day.

PAUL: And let's pretend that the cupboard is full of food. I'm hungry.

MOTHER: There! The fire is burning brightly now. We still have a few slices of bread in the cupboard and a piece of cheese. And the woman for whom I worked yesterday gave me two apples. Look, darling. This big red one is for you.

PAUL: An apple! Oh, Mother!

MOTHER: (*Laughs*) Now don't be greedy, dear. Let us give thanks first.

PAUL AND MOTHER: (*Fade*) For what we have received, dear Lord, we thank Thee.

THEODOSIA: Oh, Christmas Angel! Let me go home and ask my father to help these poor people.

ANGEL: Perhaps you yourself can help them, Theodosia. Look into your bag.

THEODOSIA: Why, the bag has opened a little, all by itself! There are silver pieces in it. I'll throw the money into the room through the broken window.

SOUND: (*Clink of falling coins*)

PAUL: Mother! Oh, Mother! Look! Silver! Now we can buy food!

MOTHER: And wood for a fire, to keep you warm and well, dear.

PAUL: And a warm coat for you, Mother, so you won't be cold. Isn't it wonderful?

MOTHER: It is wonderful, darling! I wish I could thank the good person who gave us this money. God bless him! God bless him always and always!

PAUL (*Fade*) God bless him, always and always.

ANGEL: (*Softly*) You have made them very happy, Theodosia. Let us fly on.

SOUND: (*Christmas bells*)

THEODOSIA: Why are you stopping here, Christmas Angel?

ANGEL: Look inside, Theodosia.

THEODOSIA: The room is filled with children of all ages.

ANGEL: Look again, Theodosia.

THEODOSIA: The children are crowding around a pretty young lady, (*Fade*) and she's smiling at them.

SOUND: (*Children's laughter*)

MISS MARY: (*Pleasantly*) Come, come, children! We must get down to our studies.

FIRST GIRL: Oh, Miss Mary! This is Christmas morning!

FIRST BOY: Surely you're not going to make us study today!

MISS MARY: Why not? I am not going to work today, so I have more time for you.

SECOND GIRL: But you should have a morning off.

SECOND BOY: You should, really, Miss Mary. Every morning you get up early to teach us our lessons before you go to work.

MISS MARY: It is good of you to worry about me, but I don't want a morning off. I just wish I had more time for you. It's a pity that in this town only the children of the rich can go to school. I can't even get books to teach you from.

FIRST GIRL: Oh, we don't mind learning to read from these old newspapers. It's fun, Miss Mary, seeing who can find more papers to study from.

MISS MARY: You're all doing so well really, even the youngest of you. Well, we'll have just a short lesson this morning, children. Then we'll go out into the streets and look at the people wearing all the pretty gifts they got for Christmas.

FIRST BOY: Perhaps the King and Queen will ride out in their golden coach.

SECOND GIRL: And the Princess Theodosia might be with them. (*Fade*) I hope she'll be wearing some of the lovely things she got.

THEODOSIA: Oh, Christmas Angel! I wish I could help these children and Miss Mary, too. They have so little themselves, but still they are happy to see other people have nice things.

ANGEL: Then why don't you help them, Theodosia?

THEODOSIA: I gave the little boy and his mother all the silver that was in my bag.

ANGEL: Look at your bag again, child.

THEODOSIA: Oh! It's open again, wider than it was before. And there are gold pieces in it now.

ANGEL: Will you give your gold to these children?

THEODOSIA: I should like to, but — with this gold I can buy a necklace of pearls. I do want a pearl necklace so much! Why — why — how strange!

ANGEL: What is strange, Theodosia?

THEODOSIA: When I said I wanted to buy pearls for myself, the bag closed again.

ANGEL: Perhaps it was because your heart closed and shut out the thought of other people.

THEODOSIA: Oh, I am so ashamed of myself! I have so much, and these children have so little.

ANGEL: Your bag is opening again, my child.

THEODOSIA: Yes! I can put my hand in easily and take out the gold pieces. I'll throw them down the chimney and in through the window.

SECOND BOY: Look, Miss Mary! Look at the gold pieces! It's money! Somebody has sent us a Christmas present!

MISS MARY: Did any of you children see where this money came from?

FIRST GIRL: It came down the chimney, Miss Mary. It must have been Santa Claus who threw it into the room.

FIRST BOY: But I saw it come in through the window.

MISS MARY: Well, let's not quarrel about how it got here. Somebody with a kind heart thought of us. What shall we do with the money, children?

SECOND GIRL: Miss Mary, could we have a Christmas tree, all bright and shiny like those we see through the windows of the rich houses?

SECOND BOY: (*Excited*) A Christmas tree with lighted candles!

FIRST GIRL: And red and green and blue shiny balls!

FIRST BOY: And strings of silver icicles!

SECOND GIRL: And a big silver star on the very tiptop branch!

SECOND BOY: Oh, could we have a Christmas tree, Miss Mary?

MISS MARY: Of course we must use some of this money for a Christmas tree. The good person who sent it must have meant us to have a tree. What shall we do with the rest of the money, children?

SECOND BOY: We must buy a gift for each of our mothers.

SECOND GIRL: And for our fathers, too.

MISS MARY: Oh, we won't leave out the fathers.

FIRST GIRL: And an orange to put in the toe of each baby's stocking.

MISS MARY: We'll buy those first. We can't forget the babies!

FIRST BOY: And some books, Miss Mary, so you won't have to teach us our lessons from old newspapers.

MISS MARY: (*Laugh*) Well! I'm glad somebody thought of books and lessons!

SECOND GIRL: And a present for our Miss Mary!

SECOND BOY: What shall we get for Miss Mary?

FIRST GIRL: I know! Let's get a lovely shiny necklace.

FIRST BOY: That's right! A necklace!

SECOND GIRL: A lovely shiny necklace!

MISS MARY: No, no, children! The best present I could have is to see you all so happy, and I have that now. Let's ask God to bless the kind person who sent us this money.

MISS MARY AND CHILDREN: God bless the good person, for always and always!

MUSIC: (*Christmas music as bridge*)

ANGEL: Well, Theodosia, do you begin to see what Christmas means?

THEODOSIA: I think I do, Christmas Angel. It's not what we get, but what we give, that matters.

ANGEL: Do you want to fly back to your palace now?

THEODOSIA: Oh, no, not yet. Let's keep on flying round the earth. There must be other people in need.

ANGEL: How will you help them?

THEODOSIA: Whatever magic gold there is left in my bag I will throw down to the poor and unhappy.

ANGEL: Look into your bag, Theodosia, and see what's left.

THEODOSIA: The bag is wide open now, Christmas Angel, only there isn't another coin in it.

ANGEL: Is there nothing at all in it?

THEODOSIA: No — why, yes! There is! A necklace of pearls! Oh, it's beautiful, just the kind I've been wanting!

ANGEL: Then you have nothing else to give to the poor.

THEODOSIA: (*Slowly*) Nothing but these beautiful pearls.

ANGEL: (*Gently*) It's the pearls or nothing, child.

THEODOSIA: I don't really need this necklace. I'll break the string, and drop the pearls down to the earth one by one. Here they go, falling gently.

ANGEL: And wherever a pearl falls, someone is made happy. There's a father, sad because he has been ill and out of work for a long time. He's smiling now as the pearl falls at his feet. There's a little lame boy, sitting at a window, wishing his parents could pay a doctor to make him walk again. He's smiling now as the pearl falls into his little hand. There's a little girl, shivering in a thin coat as she stands at the corner of the street, selling Christmas cards. She's laughing now as the pearl falls into her box of cards.

SOUND: (*Christmas bells up and out*)

ANGEL: Your bag is quite empty now, Theodosia. Aren't you sorry you gave away all the pearls?

THEODOSIA: No, Christmas Angel. I'm happy, very happy. I have learned the secret, the key that unlocks all treasures.

ANGEL: And what does it say on that key?

THEODOSIA: It says, "It is better to give than to receive." I shall never forget that.

ANGEL: I'm sure you won't, my child. And now you also know the true meaning of Christmas. "Peace on earth, good will to men."

THEODOSIA: "Peace on earth, good will to men."

MUSIC: (*Christmas carol up full and out*)

ANNOUNCER: And that is how Princess Theodosia learned the real meaning of Christmas. After that Christmas morning, you may be sure that she was never selfish or greedy again.

Our next tale is *Baba Yaga*, a story from Russia.

Baba Yaga

CAST

IVAN
HELENA
MOTHER
FATHER
GRANDMOTHER
WITCH
MOUSE
CAT
BIRD
ANNOUNCER
NARRATOR

SOUNDS

Milk poured into glass

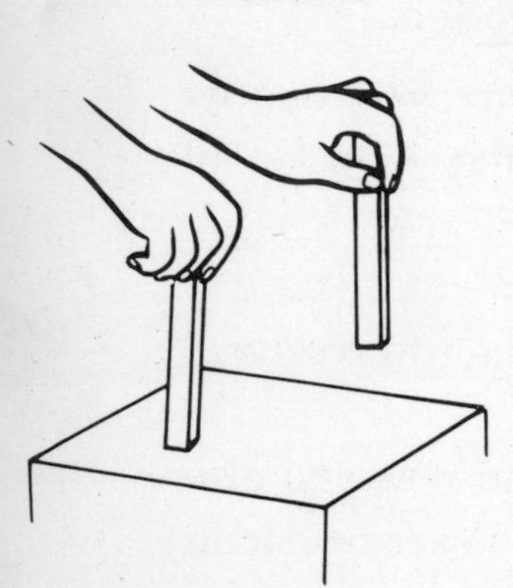

Running steps

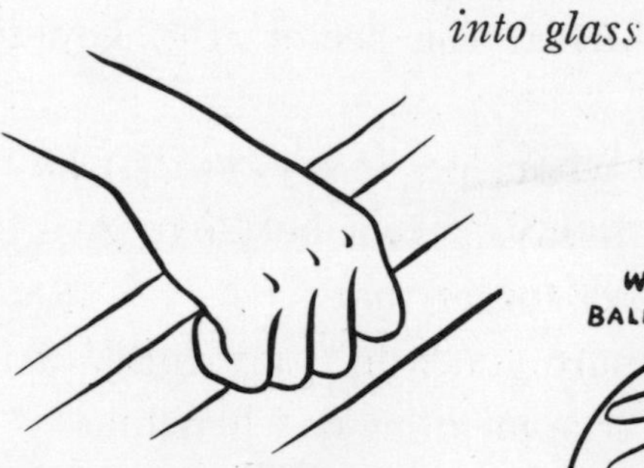

Knock at door

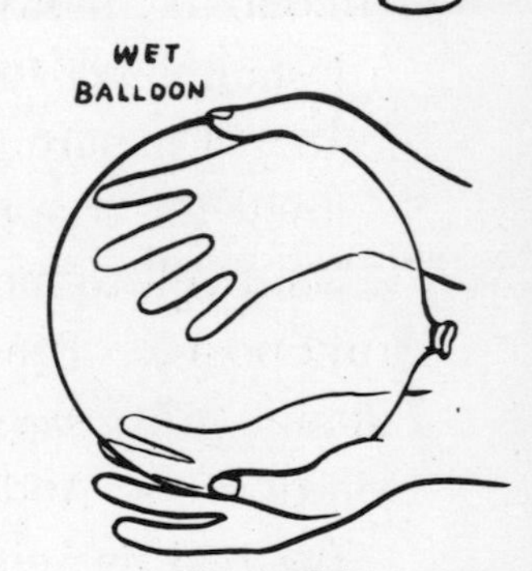

Squeaking gate

Water poured into pot

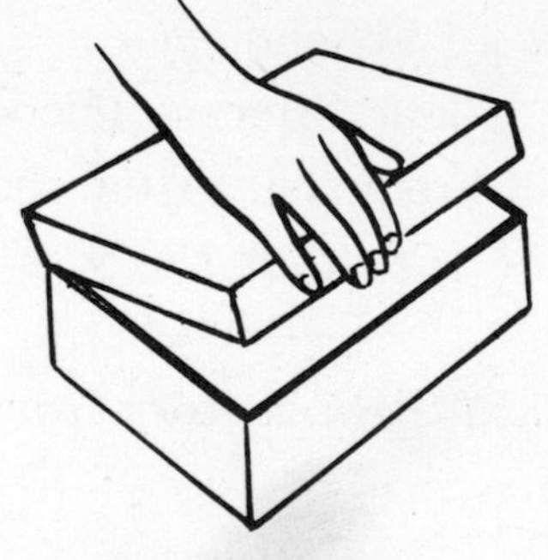

Door opened
Door closed

Slapping sound

ANNOUNCER: Hello, boys and girls! It's time for another of our *Tales from the Four Winds.* We bring you now a story that the children of Russia like to hear over and over again. The name of this story is *Baba Yaga.* Listen, and you will hear who Baba Yaga really was.

MUSIC: (*Up and out*)

NARRATOR: Long, long ago there lived in Russia a farmer who had a wife and two children, a boy named Ivan and a girl called Helena. The wife died when the children were young, and the man married again. Now, the second wife was a beautiful woman, but she was really a wicked witch, although neither the husband nor the children knew it.

When Ivan was nine years old and Helena a year younger, their stepmother decided that she didn't want them around the house any longer. She was afraid they were growing old enough to guess that she was really a wicked witch. So one day she said to them,

MOTHER: Children, it's a lovely morning. Wouldn't you like to go and play in the woods?

HELENA: Oh, that would be fun, Mother! We could look for wild strawberries.

IVAN: And perhaps I could find a frog.

HELENA: A frog! Uh!

MOTHER: Never mind looking for frogs or strawberries. I want both of you to go to your grandmother's house.

HELENA: To Grandmother's house? Oh, we love going there. She's always so nice to us.

MOTHER: I mean *my* mother, not your father's mother.

IVAN: *Your* mother? We never knew she was alive and living nearby.

MOTHER: Oh, yes, Ivan. She lives in the woods in a little house that stands on chicken feet.

IVAN: A house standing on chicken feet? We've never seen such a house around here or in the woods.

MOTHER: Well, sometimes it's hard to see the house among the trees. But you'll find it today, I know.

HELENA: Can't we go to our own grandmother — I mean, Father's mother? We know her better.

MOTHER: (*Sharp*) No! I've told my mother you'll be there today, so you must go.

HELENA: Very well, Mother.

MOTHER: You must be obedient children, and do whatever she wants you to do. Then she'll give you good things to eat, and you'll be happy while you're visiting her.

IVAN: Yes, Mother, we'll be good.

MOTHER: Start right now, Ivan and Helena. You'll have your lunch at the little house in the woods. Remember, it's the house that stands on chicken feet. (*Laugh*) The house that stands on chicken feet.

MUSIC: (*Bridge*)

NARRATOR: So Ivan and Helena started out for the woods. They didn't feel very happy about going to visit a grandmother they had never seen or heard of before. Before they reached the woods Ivan said to his sister,

IVAN: I don't feel like going to that house in the woods. Do you, Helena?

HELENA: No, Ivan, I don't. It seems strange for a house to stand on chicken feet instead of on the ground.

IVAN: Maybe this grandmother is not as nice as the one we know. This one lives in such a queer house, maybe — maybe she's a witch. Witches live in queer houses in the woods.

HELENA: Oh, Ivan! Do you think she can be a witch?

IVAN: I don't know. I was only wondering.

HELENA: Oh, I'm afraid, Ivan! Let's not go.

IVAN: We have to go, Helena.

HELENA: I wish we could ask Father what to do.

IVAN: Father always tells us to obey Mother. I'll tell you what. Let's go to our good grandmother, I mean the one we know, and ask her what to do.

HELENA: That's a good idea.

IVAN: Her house is just down the road. Let's run, Helena. I'll race you to the big tree by Grandma's door.

HELENA: All right. On your mark, get set, go!

SOUND: (*Running steps*)

IVAN: (*Breathless*) Here we are! I beat you!

HELENA: But I'm only a few steps behind you. Knock at Grandma's door, Ivan.

SOUND: (*Knock at door, door open*)

GRANDMOTHER: Why! It's Ivan and Helena! How nice of you to come to see your old Baba.

HELENA: (*As if hugging woman*) Mmm! You're just the nicest grandmother in the whole world!

GRANDMOTHER: I'm glad you think so. Come inside, darlings.

IVAN: We can't stay, Grandma. We're on our way to the forest.

GRANDMOTHER: You're going to have a little picnic in the woods? But you're not carrying any lunch. Wait. I'll pack some food for you. How lucky that I baked some cookies this morning!

HELENA: No, thank you, Grandma. We have to eat lunch at our other grandmother's house.

GRANDMOTHER: Your other Baba? I didn't know you had another.

HELENA: Neither did we, till Mother told us about her this morning.

IVAN: She said our other grandmother lives in a little house in the forest, a little house that rests on chicken feet.

GRANDMOTHER: (*Worried*) The house on chicken feet! Oh, my darlings! Is that where she lives?

IVAN: Yes. Why do you look so frightened, Grandma?

GRANDMOTHER: That house! Oh, my poor children! You are going not to a loving grandmother like myself, but to Baba Yaga, Grandmother Witch.

HELENA: A witch! Oh, Grandma!

GRANDMOTHER: If your mother sent you there, *she* must be a witch, too. And the worst of it is that I can't do anything about it. You'll have to go, or she'll find some way to make you do what she wants.

HELENA: Oh, Grandma, must we, really?

GRANDMOTHER: I'm afraid so, darlings. Now listen to me. Be kind and good to every creature you meet. Help everyone, even the weakest thing you meet.

IVAN: We'll try to remember that.

GRANDMOTHER: If you do, there is hope that you, too, will get help when you need it.

HELENA: I'm still afraid, Grandma.

GRANDMOTHER: When Baba Yaga sees you and Ivan, my dear, I'm sure she'll fall in love with you, and things won't be as bad as you fear. Come inside now.

SOUND: (*Door closed*)

GRANDMOTHER: There! I'll pack some slices of bread and meat and some fresh cookies for you to take along. While I'm doing that, you must drink a glass of milk.

SOUND: (*Milk poured*)

GRANDMOTHER: Everything will turn out all right. Let me see you smile, darlings. That's better. When I have this package of food ready, you may go on your way.

MUSIC: (*Bridge*)

NARRATOR: The good old grandmother wrapped up some slices of bread and meat and some cookies for the children, and sadly watched them start for the woods. The children soon came to the queer little house where the old witch lived. It stood on four yellow chicken feet, and at the top was a large rooster's head. The garden gates opened suddenly with a rusty squeak.

SOUND: (*Squeak of gate*)

NARRATOR: As Ivan and Helena walked towards the door of the house, the gate shut behind them. Then the door of the house opened. In the doorway stood the witch, with a mean smile on her face. The children were frightened and held tight to each other's hands. But in spite of his fright, Ivan spoke up politely.

IVAN: G-good morning, Grandmother.

WITCH: Hee, hee! My daughter's children! Come right inside, Ivan and Helena.

HELENA: Can't we — can't we visit out here, Grandmother? It's very pleasant out here in the sunshine.

WITCH: You were not sent here for a pleasant visit. You have come to work for me, and I shall set you to work at once. You, Helena, shall spin for me all day.

HELENA: Spin, Grandmother? I don't do it very well.

WITCH: You'll learn fast enough with me to teach you! And you, Ivan, shall work outdoors.

IVAN: You mean, take care of your garden?

WITCH: No, nothing as easy as that, Ivan. (*Cackling laugh*) Do you see that big wooden tub under the tree?

IVAN: Yes, Grandmother.

WITCH: Well, I want that tub filled with water from the well. But don't move the tub from that spot.

IVAN: I can lower the bucket into the well till it's filled with water, pull it up, take the bucket off the chain, and carry it over to the tub.

WITCH: There is no bucket in the well. You'll have to draw up the water in this sieve.

IVAN: But how can I carry water in a sieve? The water will run out through the holes.

WITCH: That is for you to worry about. Now, take the sieve, Ivan, and start filling the tub. Helena, go into the house and sit down at the spinning wheel. If you children do your work well, you'll get your supper at night.

HELENA: But suppose we are not able to finish our tasks, Grandmother?

WITCH: Then I shall whip you, and you will get nothing to eat. Now I must fly off on a visit to the other side of the forest. Be sure your tasks are finished by the time I return. Where's my broomstick? There it is! Whooosh! I'm off! (*Cackling laugh*)

IVAN: Come on, Helena. Now's our chance to run away from this dreadful place.

NARRATOR: So Ivan and Helena ran to the gate which had opened for them when they came, but now they could not open it. No matter how they pushed and pulled, the gate stayed tightly closed. At last Ivan said,

IVAN: Well, we had better not waste any more time trying to get out. The gate is locked, and the fence is too high for us to climb over.

HELENA: We had better get busy and try to get the work done. I know I'll never get the spinning all done, but I'll have to try.

NARRATOR: Poor Helena seated herself at the spinning wheel and began to spin. Her eyes were so full of tears that she could hardly see what she was doing. All at once she heard a squeaking and a patter of tiny feet around her. Helena looked down to see herself surrounded by a circle of little mice. One of them said (*Fade*) in a tiny voice,

MOUSE: Don't cry, little girl. Give us something to eat and perhaps we will be able to help you.

HELENA: I'll gladly give you some of the cookies our good grandmother gave my brother and me. Do you think you and your friends can help us get away from the wicked witch?

MOUSE: If we can't help you ourselves, we'll tell you somebody else who can. First, where are your cookies?

HELENA: Right here in my pocket. I'll break up a few and throw the pieces on the floor for you. Here. (*Pause*) They are good, aren't they?

MOUSE: Delicious! I'm sorry that we mice can't help you to get away, but I'll tell you what you must do. Go out to the garden and find the big black cat.

HELENA: The big black cat. And then, what?

MOUSE: If you can find some meat somewhere, give him a slice. Then he will do anything for you. The witch starves him. Ask him to help you get away. That cat is very wise and will surely know what you can do. In the meantime, we'll spin for you.

HELENA: Thank you, little mouse. You are very kind.

MOUSE: It's you who are kind, little girl. Baba Yaga, the witch, never gave us any crumbs to eat.

HELENA: I'll run right out to tell my brother, and we'll look for the big black cat.

SOUND: (*Door open*)

HELENA: Ivan! Oh, Ivan!

IVAN: (*Tired voice, off mike*) What is it, Helena?

HELENA: Oh, Ivan, you look so tired, and there's not a drop of water in the tub yet.

IVAN: (*On mike*) How can there be? I've been lowering the sieve into the well and pulling it up and running with it to the tub. But by the time I get to it, of course, all the water has run through the holes in the sieve.

HELENA: And I have done very little spinning. Oh, what will the witch say when she comes back?

IVAN: She will whip us as she said she would, and we'll get no supper.

SOUND: (*Twitter of birds*)

HELENA: Look at these birds flying around our shoulders. They seem anxious to tell us something.

BIRD: Tweet! Tweet! Listen, little children. Give us some crumbs and we will tell you how to fill the tub.

HELENA: I'll gladly give you some crumbs, little birds. I'll break up these cookies our good grandmother gave us. Here, little birds.

BIRD: Thank you, little girl. We don't eat much, but the witch never gives us anything at all. Now I'll tell the boy how to fill the tub with water.

IVAN: Tell me quickly, little bird. The witch may be back any minute. I don't want her to beat me.

BIRD: This earth is a kind of clay. Wet the clay with water and cover the bottom of the sieve with it. The clay will harden, and the sieve will become a bowl. The water will not run out of it. Then you will be able to carry water in it and fill the tub. Tweet! Tweet! We'll fly off now. Thanks for the crumbs.

IVAN: Thank you, kind little bird. Quick, Helena, help me mix this clay with water.

SOUND: (*Slapping sound*)

IVAN: Now, we'll put this clay over the bottom of the sieve. There! It's watertight. Now I can carry water in it. The bird is much more clever than we are, Helena. Now I can fill the tub easily.

SOUND: (*Water pouring into pot, in and out*)

HELENA: And now Baba Yaga won't whip you, Ivan.

IVAN: She had better not try to whip you, Helena. I won't let her.

HELENA: I'm so glad we fed the mice and the birds. They have given us helpful advice. Perhaps we really can get away from the witch. Now let's look for the big black cat. Oh, Ivan! I hope that cat can help us, as the mouse said he would.

IVAN: There's the big black cat now, climbing over the gate. Here, Pussy, Pussy, Pussy!

SOUND: (*Mew of cat fading in*)

HELENA: The mouse said that the cat is always hungry, and that if we give him some meat, he will surely help us.

IVAN: Well, we have the meat our good grandmother gave us. Nice pussy! We have some meat for you.

HELENA: Pretty pussy! Take this meat. (*Pause*) My! Look at him swallowing that meat, Ivan! He must be very hungry, poor thing.

CAT: Meow! I am always hungry. The wicked witch never gives me anything to eat. Meow!

HELENA: Pussy cat, can you help us get away from this wicked witch? We're afraid of what she may do to us.

CAT: Meow! You have been kind to me, children, so I shall help you. In a wooden box by the well you will find a towel, a comb, and a bottle of oil. Take them, and run away at once.

IVAN: But what shall we do with the towel, the comb, and the oil? Will these things make us invisible?

CAT: No, they won't do that. But when you hear Baba Yaga coming after you, throw the towel behind you.

IVAN: What will happen then, Pussy?

CAT: The towel will become a wide river, and the witch will not be able to cross. Her broomstick cannot fly over water.

HELENA: But suppose she does cross the river somehow and comes after us again? What shall we do?

CAT: Then throw the comb behind you. In its place will appear a dark, thick forest with very tall, tangled tree-tops. The witch will never be able to make her way through this thick wood. It will protect you from her, and you can safely run for home.

HELENA: But what shall we do with the bottle of oil?

CAT: Oh, I should have told you about that first. It's magic oil. Pour some of it on the lock and the hinges of the garden gate, and it will swing open for you at once. Now take these things and run off, children.

IVAN: Thank you, Pussy. We shall never forget your kindness. Quick, Helena, before the wicked witch comes back!

MUSIC: (*Bridge*)

NARRATOR: So Ivan and Helena took the towel, the comb, and the oil out of the box and ran for the gate. Ivan poured some of the oil over the lock and hinges of the gate, and it swung open for them. They ran and ran through the forest towards the sunny fields near their home. Shortly afterwards the witch came back to her house. She saw at once that the children were gone. The cat was sitting at the spinning wheel, tearing all the threads that Helena and the mice had spun. The witch began to beat the cat (*Fade*) and scold it.

WITCH: You horrid cat! Where are the children? Why did you let them run away?

CAT: Meow! Baba Yaga, I have served you well for many years, but you never gave me any food. I had to find my own. Those children gave me some good meat to eat, so I helped them. Meow!

NARRATOR: Then the witch scolded the garden gate for letting the children pass through. But the gate only swung back and forth without answering a word. Then the witch said angrily,

WITCH: I must go after those children and bring them back here. Where's my broomstick? Whoosh!

NARRATOR: So the witch jumped on her broomstick, and away she flew after the children. She went sailing over the treetops in the woods, and was soon in the fields on the other side of the forest. But the children heard her broom swishing through the air above the trees at the edge of the woods. Helena cried out,

HELENA: The witch is coming, Ivan! We must throw the towel behind us. Then there will be a river between us and the witch. Quick, Ivan! Oh, I hope the cat was right about the towel!

MUSIC: (*In quickly and out*)

NARRATOR: Ivan threw the towel behind him, and at once a river appeared, flowing swiftly on its way. The witch's broomstick could not cross over water, so she was stopped at the edge of the river. She got off the stick and hobbled along the shore till she found a spot where the river was not very deep. She waded across and started after the children again. But again the children saw her coming, and Ivan cried out,

IVAN: Baba Yaga has crossed the river, Helena! Throw the magic comb behind you! Be quick!

NARRATOR: Helena quickly threw the magic comb behind her, and at once a thick, dark wood sprang up behind the children. The witch had left her broomstick on the other side of the river, so she could not fly over this forest. She tried and tried to make her way through the tangled trees, but she could not, and at last she turned back to her house on its four yellow chicken feet.

MUSIC: (*Bridge*)

NARRATOR: The two children ran towards home until they came to the field where their father was cutting hay. He wondered what could have frightened them so.

FATHER: Helena! Ivan! What's wrong? You're all out of breath, and you look so frightened.

IVAN: Oh, Father! The witch, the wicked witch was chasing us!

HELENA: But we got away!

FATHER: The witch in the woods? But why did you go near her house?

HELENA: Mother sent us there. She said that the old woman who lived in that house was her mother.

FATHER: My wife is the daughter of that witch?

IVAN: And now we know that the old woman is our Baba Yaga, our witch grandmother.

FATHER: But are you sure that old woman was the witch?

HELENA: Oh, yes, Father. Her house stands on four yellow chicken feet, and our good grandmother said the witch lived in that house.

IVAN: And we saw the witch fly off on her broomstick.

HELENA: And we got away from her by using her magic towel and magic comb that her cat gave us.

FATHER: This is terrible! My wife is the daughter of that witch! Then she is a witch, too! That explains some strange things I have seen — her long black coat with wide sleeves, the broom in the clothes closet, the pots with queer things boiling in them.

Children, go to your good Baba and stay there till I come for you.

HELENA: But where are you going, Father?

FATHER: I am going home to send your stepmother away. She shall go and live with her wicked witch of a mother in the hut on four chicken feet. Thank Heaven, Baba Yaga had no chance to harm you, my children!

MUSIC: (*Bridge*)

NARRATOR: When the father of Ivan and Helena went back to his house, he found that his wife had taken her things and had disappeared. The good Baba came to live with the children and their father. Now that they had no fear of their stepmother or of Baba Yaga, they all lived happily together for many, many years.

MUSIC: (*Up and out*)

ANNOUNCER: And so, boys and girls, ends *Baba Yaga*, a favorite story of the children of Russia. If you should ever see a hut standing on four chicken feet, be careful! There might be a witch living in it.

The next of our *Tales from the Four Winds* is a story that the children of England like to hear. It is called *The Wise Men of Gotham.*

The Wise Men

CAST
First Man
Second Man
Third Man
Fourth Man
Fifth Man
Sixth Man
Seventh Man
Eighth Man
Ninth Man
Stranger
Mayor
Boy
King
Captain
Announcer
Narrator

SOUNDS

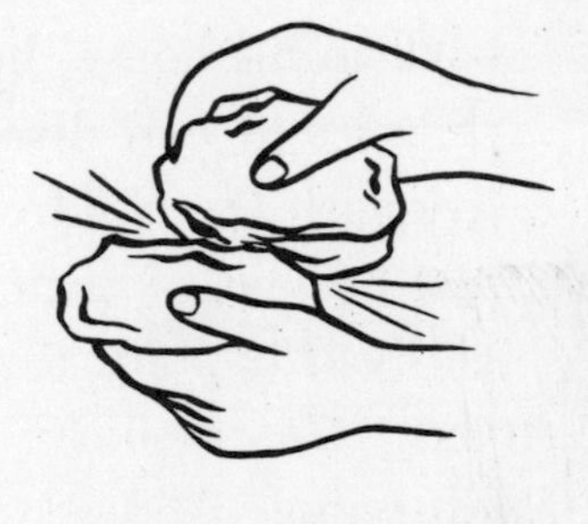

Stone against stone

Slapping sound

ANNOUNCER: Hello, boys and girls! It's story time again. Today's story is not about a fairy or a beautiful Princess. It is about some silly things and some clever things that the people of a town in old England did. Listen to the tale of *The Wise Men of Gotham*.

MUSIC: (*Up full and out*)

# of Gotham

NARRATOR: There was once a town in England called Gotham. It was a pretty town, the neighbors said. But the neighbors were never sure what to say about the people who lived in the town of Gotham. Sometimes the people of Gotham seemed to be clever about the things they said and did. But more often they appeared very foolish. We'll tell you a story or two about them, and let you make up your minds for yourselves.

MUSIC: (*Short bridge*)

NARRATOR: One fine day twelve men of Gotham went fishing together in the river that ran through their town. They fished all day long, and when evening came they started back to their homes. (*Fade*) As they walked along, one of the men said,

FIRST MAN: The water in the river was very high today, wasn't it?

SECOND MAN: Yes, friend. The melting snows have made the waters rise.

THIRD MAN: And the water was running very fast, too.

FOURTH MAN: In fact, it was really dangerous for us to go fishing there today.

FIFTH MAN: So it was. Dear me! I hope none of us has been drowned in the river while we were fishing.

SIXTH MAN: That would be terrible! Let's find out. There were twelve of us when we started out. My wife counted us. Let's count again now.

SEVENTH MAN: I'll start counting, neighbors. Henry, you're one; Peter, you are two; George, you're three; four, five, six, seven, eight, nine, ten, eleven. Dear me! Where is the twelfth man who started out with us?

EIGHTH MAN: Let me count. You're one, you're two, you're three, four, five, six, seven, eight, nine, ten, eleven. That's all I can find, too. Who is the twelfth man, the missing man?

NINTH MAN: We must find who he was, so that we can tell his poor wife that he is gone. (*Fading*) John, you're one, Henry, you're two, Peter, three ——

MUSIC: (*Few bars of music*)

NARRATOR: Well, you must have guessed by this time what was wrong with the way those men of Gotham were counting. Each man found only eleven men, because not one of them counted himself in! They went back to the river and looked up and down for their lost friend. As they stood there, a stranger came walking by. He wondered what the men were doing there. (*Fade*) He said to them,

STRANGER: Good evening, friends. You all look very sad. Has anything bad happened here?

FIRST MAN: Yes, indeed, sir. You might say a very sad thing has happened here. We were twelve men when we left our homes in Gotham to fish in the river. Now we count only eleven of us.

SECOND MAN: And so we believe, sir, that one of us must have been drowned.

STRANGER: You are men of Gotham, you say. Hm! That may explain why you can't find the twelfth man. Let me hear you count yourselves. Suppose you do it, friend.

THIRD MAN: I'll start with Peter, here. One, two, three, four, five, six, seven, eight, nine, ten, eleven! There! I told you so, sir. The twelfth man has been lost.

STRANGER: Well! (*Laugh*) What will you give me if I find the twelfth man for you?

FOURTH MAN: We'll give you all the money in our pockets, sir. It would be too bad for us to have to tell the man's wife that he has been drowned.

STRANGER: It would, indeed, especially since he is very much alive. Now, stand aside, each one of you, as I slap you on the shoulder.

SOUND: (*Loud slap on shoulder after each number*)

STRANGER: One! Two! Three! Four! Five! Six! Seven! Eight! Nine! Ten! Here's the eleventh man! And here's the twelfth man!

FIFTH MAN: If I am the twelfth man, then I am the man who was lost. Thank you, sir, for finding me!

ALL: Thank you, sir, for finding our lost neighbor!

MUSIC: (*Bridge*)

NARRATOR: Well, that's one story they tell about the men of Gotham. Here is another story. This one may make you wonder if they really were as foolish as they often seemed to be. One day the people of Gotham heard that the King was going to pass through their town on his way from London to another of his castles. This news did not please the people at all. They did not like the King. He was cruel and he made all the people pay much money in taxes. If he came through their town, they knew they would have to find food for him and his soldiers, and perhaps give up their beds for a night.

They also knew that whenever the King saw anything he liked, he took it without asking. Nobody dared refuse him anything. Wasn't he the King? The men of Gotham met in their town hall to talk the matter over. (*Fade*) The Mayor sat in his big chair on the platform and started the meeting.

MAYOR: Men of Gotham, we have come together this evening to try to find a way of keeping the King out of our town. Has anybody any idea as to how this can be done?

FIRST MAN: Let's all stand in the road so that the King can't pass. Then he will have to turn around and go back to London.

MAYOR: I'm afraid that would not stop the King. He would simply order his horsemen to ride over us, and we would have to run to keep from being killed.

FIRST MAN: That's true. The King is a very cruel man. I see that my idea is not as good as I thought it was.

MAYOR: Does anybody else have any ideas? (*Slight pause*) No? Well, I have thought of something. Let's chop down a great many trees and lay them across the road leading into Gotham. This will block the road, and the King and his men will see that they will have a hard time getting into our town. Then, I am sure, the King will turn around and take another road.

VOICES: Good! A fine idea! Let's block the road!

MAYOR: I'm glad you like my idea. Tomorrow morning we shall all meet in the woods outside the town and start chopping down the trees for the road block. This meeting is over now. Remember, we meet at the edge of the woods at six tomorrow morning.

MUSIC: (*Bridge*)

NARRATOR: And so at six o'clock the next morning, all the men of Gotham met at the edge of the woods. Each man had his axe with him. Soon the countryside around the town rang with the sound of their axes. In a few hours the main highway and all the narrow roads that led into the town of Gotham were filled with logs and broken branches. Then the men went back to town, leaving an older boy to stand by and report what happened when the King came.

MUSIC: (*Short bridge*)

NARRATOR: Shortly after noon the King and his men came riding up the road. They galloped swiftly along, and then they had to stop. They could ride no farther, for the road was blocked with logs and branches. The King was very angry. He looked around and spied the boy, standing by a tree stump. The King roared out at him,

KING: You, there! Come here, boy!

BOY: (*Slightly off mike*) Y-yes, your Majesty.

KING: Who blocked this road?

BOY: (*Frightened*) I-I didn't do it, your Majesty.

KING: Nonsense! Tell me who did. Was it the men of the next town who chopped these trees down and blocked my way? Tell me the truth, or I'll have you whipped till you do.

BOY: Yes, your Majesty, it was the men of Gotham who blocked the road.

KING: Ah! I have heard that the people of Gotham are stupid. Now they shall see what being stupid has done for them. Go back, boy, and tell the men of Gotham that tomorrow morning my soldiers will ride into their town and cut off the noses of all the men. Do you hear me?

BOY: Yes, your Majesty. I'll tell them. (*Fade*) I'm going! I'm going!

KING: I'll teach those men of Gotham how to respect their King! Now, Captain, order your men to clear this road!

MUSIC: (*Bridge*)

NARRATOR: But it was no easy task to clear that road of all the logs and fallen trees, though the soldiers worked hard. The King soon grew impatient and turned around and went back to his palace in London.

In the meantime, the boy ran back to the Mayor of Gotham and told him what the King had said. The Mayor called the men together at once. You can be sure they were all very much frightened and wondered what was to be done. (*Fade*) As the Mayor said,

MAYOR: We thought up a good plan to keep the King out of our town. Now we must think up a good plan to keep the King from cutting off our noses.

VOICES: We must find a plan! We must keep our noses!

FIRST MAN: Your Honor the Mayor, it was you who thought up the plan to block the road and so keep the King out of Gotham. You are the only one of us who sometimes has an idea. Why don't you try to think and tell us what to do?

MAYOR: Well, I have thought of something. I have noticed that many a man has been punished because he was too clever for the people around him. But I have never seen a man harmed because he was a fool and didn't have much sense.

VOICES: True! That's right! True!

MAYOR: And so, I think that when the King's soldiers come, we should all act like fools, as if we didn't have a grain of sense in our heads.

SECOND MAN: That shouldn't be too hard for us to do.

VOICES: Good! Good! We'll all act like fools!

MAYOR: Break up into small groups now and think what you can do when the King's men come.

MUSIC: (*Bridge*)

NARRATOR: Very early the next morning a captain with a band of the King's soldiers rode through the woods and along the road to Gotham. Just before they reached the town they saw a strange sight. Some old men were rolling big stones up a hill, while a group of young men stood at the foot of the hill and grunted very loudly as if they were doing the heavy work.

SOUND: (*Stone against stone, loud grunts*)

NARRATOR: The Captain stopped his horsemen and watched for a few minutes. Then he called out to one of the young men,

CAPTAIN: Young man, what are you men doing with those stones?

FIRST MAN: Why, the sun has not come up yet. We want to make the sun rise, and so our fathers are rolling these stones uphill, to make the sun rise above them.

CAPTAIN: You foolish fellow! The sun will rise when it is time for it to rise. Don't you know *you* can't do anything to make the sun rise?

FIRST MAN: Can't we really? We thought we could.

CAPTAIN: And why are you young men grunting and groaning?

FIRST MAN: Well, our fathers are working so hard that they haven't time to grunt and groan. So we are doing it for them.

CAPTAIN: The old men work, and the young men stand by and grunt! What a pack of fools these men of Gotham are! Forward, men!

MUSIC: (*Bridge*)

NARRATOR: The Captain and his men rode on. By and by they came to a field where a number of men were building a stone wall. The soldiers could see that the men were planning other walls to form a large open square. The Captain stopped his men and called out,

CAPTAIN: Ho, there! What are you men building?

SECOND MAN: Why, can't you see, sir? We are building a high wall. We are going to build four walls like this, in a square.

CAPTAIN: What for? Is this to be a large building — a town hall, or a theatre?

SECOND MAN: Oh, no, sir. We are not putting up a building, just four high walls.

CAPTAIN: But what will you do with this empty space inside the walls?

SECOND MAN: Why, sir, there is a lark which has a nest in this field. We are building these walls around the field to keep the bird from leaving us. We want it to stay with us always.

CAPTAIN: (*Hearty laugh*) You foolish fellows!

SECOND MAN: Why do you call us foolish fellows, sir?

CAPTAIN: Because you are! Don't you know that you can't fence in a bird?

SECOND MAN: We can't?

CAPTAIN: Of course not! The bird will fly over the top of your walls no matter how high you build them.

SECOND MAN: We never thought of that! How very wise you are, sir! Do you think we had better stop working on these walls then?

CAPTAIN: You are wasting your time and your stones. What fools you men of Gotham are! Forward, men! Let's get to the town.

MUSIC: (*Bridge*)

NARRATOR: So the Captain and the King's soldiers galloped on towards the town. By and by they spied a man walking right in the middle of the road. He was carrying a large flat piece of wood on his back. The Captain ordered his men to halt, (*Fade*) and he called out to the man,

CAPTAIN: Ho, there! Where are you going with that heavy piece of lumber on your back?

THIRD MAN: This is not just a piece of wood I am carrying, sir. You will see that if you look closely.

CAPTAIN: Now that I look at it more closely, I see that it is a door. I can see a door knob and a lock under the knob.

THIRD MAN: That's right, sir. This is the door to my house.

CAPTAIN: The door to your house? Where are you taking it? Are you building a new house somewhere?

THIRD MAN: Oh, no, sir. I am not rich enough to build a new house. You see, sir, I am going on a three days' journey.

CAPTAIN: But what has the door to do with your journey?

THIRD MAN: Why, don't you see, sir? I am afraid that while I am gone a thief might break into my house and rob me. If I carry my door with me, no thief can break the lock and get in.

CAPTAIN: (*Hearty laugh*) What a foolish fellow you are!

THIRD MAN: Why am I a foolish fellow, sir?

CAPTAIN: Because it would have been safer for you to carry your money with you and leave the door at home.

THIRD MAN: Do you really think so, sir? I never thought of that. What a wise man you are, sir!

CAPTAIN: Are all you men of Gotham as foolish as the ones I met along the road this morning?

THIRD MAN: I don't know whom you met, sir, but we are all pretty much alike in our town.

CAPTAIN: Well, there must be some people in the town with sense in their heads. Somebody had the thought of blocking the road so that the King could not pass. Let's ride on, men. We have the King's orders. Forward!

MUSIC: (*Bridge*)

NARRATOR: So the King's soldiers, with the Captain at the head, galloped on towards Gotham. But everyone they met was doing some silly thing. When the soldiers came to the first street of the town the Captain stopped them. (*Fade*) With a broad smile on his face he said,

CAPTAIN: Men, we shall not go into the town. I have never met such a pack of fools as these men of Gotham. I believe it would be a shame to harm such simple, foolish people. I shall go back to the King and tell him what we have seen. I'm sure even the King will be amused by their doings and will change his mind about cutting off their noses. About face! Back to London we go!

MUSIC: (*Bridge*)

NARRATOR: And back to London galloped the soldiers. The Captain told the King that Gotham was a town of simple, silly fools who did not know what they were doing. The King laughed at the queer things his soldiers saw the people of Gotham doing, (*Fade*) and he said,

KING: Since those men of Gotham are only silly fools, let them keep their noses. I shall not harm them.

MUSIC: (*Up full and out*)

ANNOUNCER: So you see that even if the King and the Captain didn't think so, there were some wise men in Gotham after all.

Our next tale comes from Germany. It is called *The Pied Piper*. Be sure to listen. We know you will like it.

The Pied Piper

CAST

BOY	MOTHER
GIRL	FIRST COUNCILLOR
MAYOR	SECOND COUNCILLOR
SENTRY	FIRST WOMAN
FIRST MAN	SECOND WOMAN
SECOND MAN	THIRD WOMAN
PIPER	NARRATOR
FRANZ	ANNOUNCER

SOUNDS

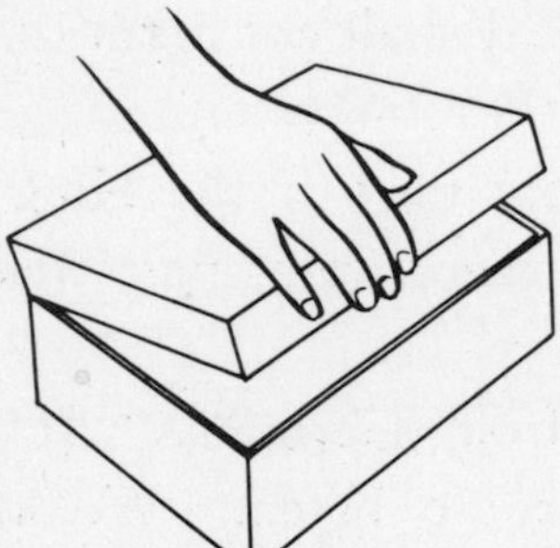

Door open
Door shut

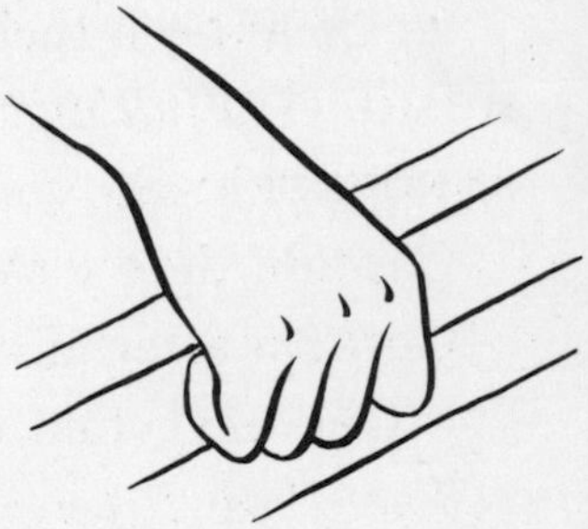

Knock at door

Sound of pipe

Church bells

ANNOUNCER: Hello, boys and girls. It's story time. This tale you will hear comes from Germany. It tells about some people who didn't keep a promise and of how they were punished. Listen to *The Pied Piper*.

MUSIC: (*Up and out*)

NARRATOR: There wasn't a prettier town in all Germany than the little town of Hamelin. A deep river flowed past the town, and a tall tree-covered mountain at its back kept the harsh winds away. It was a very pleasant place to live. But at one time, over five hundred years ago, the people of Hamelin were leading most uncomfortable lives. Why? Well, because Hamelin was overrun by rats.

GIRL: Rats! They fought the dogs and killed the cats,

BOY: And bit the babies in their cradles,

GIRL: And ate the cheeses out of the vats,

BOY: And licked the soup from the cooks' own ladles.

GIRL: Split open the kegs of salted sprats,

BOY: Made nests inside men's Sunday hats,

GIRL: And even spoiled the women's chats,
By drowning their speaking
With shrieking and squeaking
In fifty different sharps and flats.

MUSIC: (*Short bridge*)

NARRATOR: Yes, that was what made the people of Hamelin so miserable — the rats. In their homes and at their work the people suffered from the great number of rats that walked boldly through the streets and houses. There seemed to be no way of killing them off or driving them out. One day as the Mayor was sitting at his desk in the Town Hall, there was a knock at the door. (*Fade*) He called out,

MAYOR: Come in!

SOUND: (*Door open*)

MAYOR: What is it, sentry?

SENTRY: There are two men outside, your Honor, who say they must speak to you.

MAYOR: What about?

SENTRY: I don't know, your Honor. They say they were chosen by the people to call on you.

MAYOR: Very well, sentry. Show them in. (*Short pause*) Good morning, gentlemen. Come in and have a seat.

SOUND: (*Door shut*)

FIRST MAN: Thank you, your Honor.

MAYOR: Now, what can I do for you, gentlemen?

FIRST MAN: The people of Hamelin have sent us to speak for them on a most important matter.

MAYOR: And what is this most important matter?

SECOND MAN: The rats, Mr. Mayor. You must rid Hamelin of the rats that make life miserable for us.

MAYOR: The rats again! The Town Councillors and I have tried to get rid of them.

FIRST MAN: Then you must try harder. We elected you to make the town a good place to live in.

MAYOR: We have made Hamelin a safe place to live by driving away all thieves and other bad men.

SECOND MAN: True. But these rats are worse than any thieves who might steal gold or silver. They will force us to leave our homes and go to some other town to live if you don't do something about them very soon.

MAYOR: But, gentlemen, we have done our best.

FIRST MAN: That is not good enough. The people chose you and the Town Councillors because we believed you were wise men. We are tired of paying our good money to town officials who don't know how to get rid of rats.

MAYOR: We have done everything possible. There never were such big, fierce, and fearless rats!

SECOND MAN: The people believe it is your duty to find a way to get rid of the rats. If you can't, *we* will get rid of *you* and choose men with better brains.

MAYOR: But, gentlemen ——!

FIRST MAN: The people sent us here to warn you. Either you rid us of these pests, or Hamelin will have a new mayor and a new group of Town Councillors. Good morning, your Honor!

SOUND: (*Door open and shut noisily*)

MAYOR: Dear me! What a mess this is! (*Calls*) Sentry!

SOUND: (*Door open quietly*)

SENTRY: Yes, your Honor?

MAYOR: You hear the people talking as you walk about the town. Do you think the people really mean this talk about a new mayor?

SENTRY: The people are very much upset by this time, your Honor, and they are likely to do anything to get rid of the rats.

MAYOR: My head aches with trying to think.

SOUND: (*Gentle knock at door*)

MAYOR: What's that? Is that a knock at the door or a rat? Anything that sounds like a rat makes my heart go pit-a-pat.

SOUND: (*Knock repeated*)

SENTRY: I'll see who it is, sir.

MAYOR: Let him in, whoever he is. Well! Bless my soul! What a strange figure of a man! Tall and thin as a bean pole. Shut the door, sentry, but remain on guard.

SOUND: (*Door shut*)

MAYOR: You dress in queer fashion, stranger. Your clothes are half yellow, half red, like the King's jester in my grandfather's time.

PIPER: That is why men call me the Pied Piper, because of the different colors of my clothing.

MAYOR: Why have you come to Hamelin? What do you want of me?

PIPER: If you please, Mr. Mayor, I have come to rid your town of its rats.

MAYOR: What! Did I hear you correctly? Did you say you have come to rid us of the rats?

PIPER: Yes, your Honor. I know I can do it.

MAYOR: How? Have you a special poison or a new trap?

PIPER: Neither. I am able, by a secret charm, to make all living things follow me — all creatures that creep or swim or fly or run.

MAYOR: And do you use this secret charm on any living things, whenever you feel like it?

PIPER: Oh, no, your Honor. I use it only on creatures that harm people. You see this pipe tied to the red and yellow scarf around my neck?

MAYOR: Yes, and I can see that your fingers are impatient to pick it up and play on it.

PIPER: By playing a tune on this pipe of mine, I have rid other towns of mice and rats and other harmful creatures. I can rid Hamelin of its rats too, if you will pay the price I ask.

MAYOR: If you will free Hamelin of its rats, the Town Council will gladly pay you any price you ask.

PIPER: For this service I ask one thousand guilders, your Honor.

MAYOR: One thousand guilders! I'll be glad to pay you fifty thousand out of the town money if you can do away with these pests.

PIPER: One thousand guilders is all I ask. Is it a bargain, your Honor?

MAYOR: It is a bargain, Piper. How happy we'll all be to see the rats leaving Hamelin!

MUSIC: (*Sound of pipe up and fade out under narrator's speech*)

NARRATOR: The Pied Piper smiled, and his blue eyes twinkled. He stepped into the street. He put his pipe to his lips and played a strange, sweet tune. Before he had blown a dozen notes, there was a mumbling and a grumbling and a squeaking, and the rats started tumbling out of the shops and houses. They came singly and by families, by the tens and by the twenties, gray rats, black rats, mother rats, father rats, and baby rats. The people, too, came out to watch this strange sight. (*Fade*) It was a very pleasant sight to them.

FRANZ: Look, Mother! All the rats are coming out of our house!

MOTHER: Isn't it wonderful, Franz, to see them going at last! Now we shall be able to live in comfort.

FRANZ: They're all running after the Piper.

MOTHER: Yes, dear. The Piper seems to have some magic power that makes the rats follow him.

FRANZ: Let's follow along, Mother, and see where he takes the rats.

MOTHER: Walk slowly, dear. Be careful of your weak leg.

FRANZ: Do rats really like music so much?

MOTHER: I don't know. But this is surely a magic tune the Piper is playing for them.

FRANZ: I wonder what the rats hear in that song?

MOTHER: Well, I suppose it sings to them of cupboard doors left open and shelves full of everything rats love to eat.

FRANZ: Shelves full of cheese and apples and bacon?

MOTHER: And open jars of peas and beans and, perhaps, some prunes.

FRANZ: And no cat to scare them away.

MOTHER: That must be a rat's idea of Heaven!

FRANZ: I wonder where the Piper is taking them, Mother?

MOTHER: He's turning down this street. It leads to the river. Look, dear! He's going right down to the bank of the river! The rats are following him!

FRANZ: He's going to drown them!

MOTHER: Yes! The Piper is stepping aside, and — the rats are keeping straight on into the river!

FRANZ: The river is full of rats! They're drowning, every one of them! No more rats! Hurrah!

SOUND: (*Church bells up and under mother's speech*)

MOTHER: Listen! The church bells are ringing! It's a great day for Hamelin! The rats are gone! Let's go to the square in front of the Town Hall, Franz. Everybody will be going there.

SOUND: (*Church bells up full and out*)

VOICES: Hurrah! The rats are gone! The town is free of rats at last! The rats are gone! Hurrah!

MAYOR: (*Above voices*) People of Hamelin! (*Voices out*) People of Hamelin! Go back to your houses and make them clean and safe again. Clear out the nests where the rats have lived. Fill up the holes in the walls. Let there be no trace left in all Hamelin of the pests that almost drove us from our homes.

VOICES: Hurrah! No more rats in our homes! Three cheers for the Mayor! Hurrah! Hurrah! Hurrah!

MAYOR: Thank you, my good people.

PIPER: If you please, your Honor ——

MAYOR: Who is interrupting my speech? Oh, it's you, the Pied Piper.

PIPER: Yes, your Honor. It's time for my ——

MAYOR: You did a good job of getting rid of the rats.

PIPER: I told you I would. And now, if you please, my thousand guilders.

MAYOR: A thousand guilders. Ahem! That's a very large sum of money.

PIPER: You promised it, if I would get rid of the rats.

MAYOR: But a thousand guilders! I'll ask my Town Councillors here at my side. What do you say, Councillor?

FIRST COUNCILLOR: That is a very high price to pay a man, your Honor, just for playing a tune on a pipe.

SECOND COUNCILLOR: (*Low*) Your Honor, think how much wine we could buy for our Council dinners with half that sum.

MAYOR: You're right, Councillor. Why should we pay a thousand guilders to this beggar?

FIRST COUNCILLOR: Besides, your Honor, the rats are gone now. We saw them drown. The Piper played them into the river, but he can't play them alive again.

MAYOR: That makes sense, Councillor. He cannot bring them back to life. They're gone forever.

FIRST COUNCILLOR: Then offer the Piper a small sum for his trouble, your Honor, and send him away.

PIPER: I'm waiting, your Honor, for my thousand guilders.

MAYOR: Surely you don't expect me to give you all that money, Piper.

PIPER: That was our bargain. One thousand guilders.

MAYOR: But I never meant it. I was only jesting.

PIPER: Oh, no, you were not jesting, your Honor. You were so anxious for me to get rid of those rats that you offered me fifty thousand. But I won't ask for that, only for the one thousand I asked at the time.

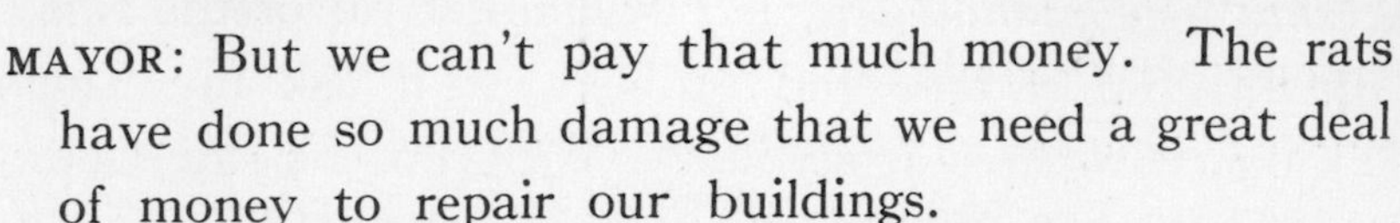

MAYOR: But we can't pay that much money. The rats have done so much damage that we need a great deal of money to repair our buildings.

PIPER: You are wasting my time, Mr. Mayor. I must be on my way to Persia. I have an appointment with the Sultan of Bagdad. Give me my thousand guilders.

MAYOR: We'll give you fifty guilders.

PIPER: I carried out my part of the bargain and got rid of the rats for you. Now you must keep yours and pay me the money you promised.

MAYOR: I tell you I was only joking. Take the fifty guilders and be off.

PIPER: Not a copper less than the thousand will I take, your Honor. If you make me angry, I'll pipe another tune, and you'll be sorry.

MAYOR: What! Do you dare to threaten me, the Mayor of Hamelin? You, a beggar with only a pipe and a red and yellow suit of clothes to his name?

PIPER: All I am asking is that you keep your promise.

MAYOR: The rats are gone forever, drowned in the river. Suppose I refuse to pay you anything at all now?

PIPER: I tell you, your Honor, if you do that, I'll play a tune that will make you sorry the rest of your life.

MAYOR: Play your tune, then! Do your worst! Not one guilder shall you get!

PIPER: Very well, Mr. Mayor. I gave you fair warning.

MUSIC: (*Sound of pipe up and fade under narrator's speech*)

NARRATOR: The Pied Piper left the Town Hall Square. Once more he put his pipe to his lips. This time the music was soft and sweet, yet merry too. The Piper had no sooner started playing when along came the children, skipping and laughing and clapping their hands with delight.

SOUND: (*Laughter of children in briefly and fade out*)

NARRATOR: The bright-eyed little girls with their golden curls, the rosy-cheeked boys, all danced after the Piper as he played his wonderful music. At first the people laughed, too, when they saw their children dancing so gaily. But soon the parents began to grow frightened. (*Fade*) They called after the children.

MOTHER: Come back, Franz! Come back here!

FIRST WOMAN: Gretchen, darling! Come back to Mother!

SECOND WOMAN: Otto! Otto! Don't follow the Piper! Come back here! Come back!

THIRD WOMAN: Some of you men, run after the children! Make them turn back! Take them away from the Piper!

FIRST MAN: I can't move!

SECOND MAN: I can't, either! The Piper has bewitched us!

MOTHER: Mayor, send your police to make the Piper bring our children back!

MAYOR: None of us can stir a step. The Piper has bewitched us all! My own children, too, are following after him.

FIRST WOMAN: Where is he taking our children?

SECOND WOMAN: He's turning down the street to the river! He'll drown our children as he drowned the rats!

MAYOR: Oh, why didn't we pay him the money? What's a thousand guilders compared to our children?

FIRST WOMAN: Look! The Piper is turning away from the river. He's going towards the mountain!

SECOND WOMAN: Then our children are safe! They will never be able to climb over the top.

THIRD WOMAN: The Piper will have to stop playing, and our children will come back to us.

FIRST MAN: Look! The mountain is opening! A door in the side of the mountain is opening!

FIRST WOMAN: Our children are following the Piper inside the mountain. Come back, children!

VOICES: The mountain is opening! The Piper is leading the children inside the mountain! Oh! Oh! Come back, children! Can't you hear us? Come back!

MAYOR: The mountain has shut fast! We shall never see our children again! Why didn't we pay the Piper? Why didn't we keep our promise?

VOICES: (*Despairing*) Oh! Our children! Our children are gone!

MUSIC: (*Bridge*)

NARRATOR: But not all the children had disappeared inside the mountain. As the people of Hamelin stood weeping and staring in horror at the mountain, a little boy limped slowly back to the Square. It was Franz, the carpenter's little lame boy. (*Fade*) His mother hugged him tightly to her as she said,

MOTHER: Franz, my darling! How happy I am to have you back! You're a good boy for not going with the others.

FRANZ: I wanted to go with the other children, Mother. I didn't want to come back here.

MOTHER: But you heard me calling and you listened. You didn't go inside the mountain with the Piper.

FRANZ: I didn't hear anyone calling. I heard only the lovely things that the Piper's music promised me. I didn't go inside with the others because I am lame. (*Weeping*) I couldn't walk fast enough. The door in the mountain shut before I could get inside.

MOTHER: Oh, my darling! For once I am happy that you are lame. What did the Piper's music promise you?

FRANZ: It sang of a lovely land where everything was strange and beautiful, where the grass was carpeted with bright flowers, and the trees were full of sweet fruits. There the sparrows were as large and beautiful as peacocks, and the honey bees had no stings. And just as the music was promising me that my lame foot would be well again and I could run and play like the other children, the door of the mountain closed, and I was left outside. (*Weeps*) And now I'll never see that beautiful land, and my foot will never be well!

MOTHER: Oh, my little Franz!

MAYOR: The little Franz is the only child left in Hamelin.

FRANZ: I'll never see my playmates again! I'll have nobody to play with! I wish I had gone with the Piper!

MAYOR: People of Hamelin! Today we have been taught a lesson that we shall never forget. How costly a broken promise may be! Let us write this sad story so that others born after us may read it and know that a promise given must always be kept.

MUSIC: (*Bridge*)

NARRATOR: And so the people of Hamelin wrote the story of the Pied Piper and the lost children of Hamelin on a stone column. They placed the column opposite the spot where the mountain had opened. On the windows of the church they painted pictures of their children following the Piper. And they say that after that, no man or woman of Hamelin ever broke a promise.

MUSIC: (*Up full and out*)

ANNOUNCER: And so ends the story of the man who could charm animals and children with the music of his magic pipe.

To the Teacher

Objectives

The use of the books in the series, *Tales from the Four Winds*, will achieve these worthwhile objectives: it will contribute to your pupils' literary background, will aid understanding of other peoples, and will provide a well-motivated and functional program in oral reading for both normal and remedial groups.

Building Literary Background

The stories in these books are mainly folk tales, some of them the familiar old favorites, others less familiar selections from the folk literature of various countries. Also included are some modern stories which have been so popular as to deserve a place in our children's literary background.

Faced with a crowded school program, the modern teacher understandably has difficulty finding the time and opportunity for the introduction of the old classics with which she feels her pupils should become familiar. In these books you will find such stories presented in a new and interesting form. They are written in a vocabulary which will be easily handled by the children for whom the books are intended.

Aiding Understanding of Other Peoples

The tales used in these books represent the folk lore of many different nations. By calling the children's attention to the fact that their favorite stories come from many lands, and by pointing out the similarities between stories from different countries, you will help to establish the understanding that people all over the world have many of the same basic interests, likes, and dislikes that we have. Emphasizing the likenesses between groups rather than their differences helps to form a feeling of fellowship for people of other lands.

Building an Oral Reading Program

In addition to contributing to literary background and to international good-feeling, these books supply an excellent source of supplementary oral reading material. The need for good teaching of oral reading is recognized by all educators. Dr. Paul McKee says, ". . . skillful teaching of oral reading is essential to the child's well-balanced growth in the power to read."[1]

The tales in this series have been dramatized and are presented in the form of drama best known to modern children, the radio play. The dramatized form has a distinct advantage over the narrative form as material to be read orally, because it automatically creates the audience situation, without which oral reading becomes much less purposeful.

When a radio play is presented, the listener sees no costumes, no scenery, no facial expressions or gestures to help him grasp the spirit of the play and the meaning of the dialogue. His understanding and enjoyment of the play must depend completely on the clarity and expression with which the actors read their lines. Oral reading of this type of material, therefore, places a premium on correct pronunciation, clear enunciation, and good expression. Because a child reads the part of only one person in a radio play, he finds it easy to identify himself with that character and thus read the lines with adequate feeling. As most of the speeches are short, the young reader is much less self-conscious than he would be if he were reading a long prose selection for others.

The dramatic form is an excellent one for group activity. The fact that each person taking part must watch

[1] McKee, Paul, *The Teaching of Reading*. Houghton Mifflin Co., Boston, 1948.

for his own lines keeps each one alert and helps to maintain the interest of the entire group.

Through radio plays it is possible to use oral reading to entertain others. One group within the class may present a play for the rest of the class. Any one of the plays might be presented as a class project for other classes within the school. A radio play eliminates any necessity for costumes or scenery, as well as that of the actors' learning their lines verbatim. This type of program is especially good as a confidence builder for the shy, self-conscious child who dreads facing an audience.

These books will also prove useful in working with remedial groups. The short speeches are even more of an advantage in the remedial situation, because they help to relax the tension which many remedial readers feel when doing any oral reading at all. The short speech does not allow time for the tension to build up and become a block to performance.

The dramatic form simplifies the task of holding the attention of all members of the group, a task which is much more difficult with a remedial group than with a group of good readers. Using one of these plays, a remedial group might prepare a program for other children. The performance will give the members a sense of achievement in reading instead of the feeling of failure which they have experienced so frequently in the past.

Equipment

The simple sound effects suggested for these plays and the use of music between parts of the plays add to the interest by making the performances seem like the radio programs which children listen to and enjoy. While the plays may be read as a class activity without the sound effects or music, you will find that the added interest which sound effects and music bring to their performance is well worth the trouble of getting them ready beforehand. All the materials required for the sound effects are easily obtained, and the manipulation of the properties is never complicated. The children will enjoy experimenting in order to obtain the desired effect, and they may find substitutes for the materials suggested in the book. The music need not be elaborate. It may be supplied by a record player and records or by children singing or humming a part of a song which they already know.

To add to the illusion of a radio presentation, a make-believe radio studio may be constructed. A screen or curtain may be placed across one corner of the room in order to conceal the actors, a table and other properties for the sound man, and any musical equipment which is used. If you prefer, a screen which will rest on top of a table may be made by using cardboard from large cartons. A cloth hung from the edge of the table to the floor will conceal the actors' feet.

A make-believe microphone might be placed in the "studio." It can be made from an empty tin can, or from a chalk or cigar box painted silver. A hole should be made in the bottom of the microphone so that it will fit on a stand. For a stand you could use a discarded music stand or a broomstick set in a wooden base.

Vocabulary

The objectives mentioned above are made easy of achievement because of the limited vocabulary used in the books. In *The Crowded House and Other Tales*, ninety-three per cent of the 1796 different words used in the scripts are within a fifth grade vocabulary, as checked with *Stone's Graded Vocabulary for Primary Reading* and the Thorndike-Lorge *Teacher's Word List of 30,000 Words*.

Acknowledgments

The author wishes to make grateful acknowledgment to James F. Macandrew, Coordinator of Broadcasting for the Board of Education of the City of New York, for his encouragement and enthusiasm, for reading the section on production, and for contributing the directions for building a make-believe microphone.

Thanks are also offered to Dorothy Klock of the production staff of WNYE, whose imaginative production of many of these scripts has taught the author much about the possibilities of educational radio for younger children.

The author is deeply indebted to her sisters, Celia and Jeanne, whose unfailing thoughtfulness made possible the leisure to write these scripts.

Illustrators

Clever Manka, *The Three Golden Oranges*, *The Feast of Lanterns*, *The Crowded House*, and *The Wise Men of Gotham* were illustrated by Bruno Frost; *One-Inch Fellow*, *The Ugly Duckling*, *The Golden Touch*, and *The Christmas Angel* by Violet La Mont; *The Pied Piper* and *Baba Yaga* by Eleanor Dart; *The Young Paul Bunyan* by Anne Fleur.